Thomas Slapp's Booke of Physicke

edited by Pip Wright

ISBN 978-0-9548298-7-2

Published by **Pawprint Publishing**
14, Polstead Close, Stowmarket, Suffolk   IP14 2PJ

Acknowledgements
Special thanks are owed to Desiree Shelley, Medical Herbalist,
who helped me to identify many of the items here,
and their traditional use.
Thanks to Elizabeth Nelson and Anne Morgan Hughes
(Blackcat Books) for permission to publish this text.
Also thanks to Megan Dennis and the staff at Gressenhall Museum,
the Barker family at Lodge Farm Museum, Westhorpe, Suffolk,
Mrs. Jordan at Brook Farm Museum, Buxhall,
Brian Buffery for permission to use the
splendid bee-skep picture on page 65
The Cambridge Folk Museum,
All at Pakenham Watermill,
The owners and staff at Kentwell Hall,
and finally, Lynn Sargeant for permission to publish
details from her late father's notebook

Front cover picture - The walled garden at Benhall, Suffolk,

The physicke garden at Felbrigg Hall, Norfolk

Other books by Pip Wright

Lydia

Death Recorded

I Read it in the local Rag
(pub. by Poppyland Publishing)

Exploring Suffolk by Bus Pass

Books by Pip & Joy Wright

**The Amazing Story of John Heigham Steggall,
'The Suffolk Gipsy'**

Newspapers in Suffolk (6 vols)

Grave Reports

Witches in and around Suffolk

Bygone Cotton

See all these at
www.pipwright.com

&

The Diary of a Poor Suffolk Woodman
(with Léonie Robinson, pub. by Poppyland Publishing)
See **www.poppyland.co.uk**

In March 2009, an amazing book came up for auction. Handwritten and running to just 64 pages, it was mostly concerned with patent cures and remedies for all manner of complaints. Added to these were recipes for preserves, cakes and meals. It has been faithfully transcribed here along with certain explanations as to some of the ingredients described.

Little punctuation was used, but such as did appear is included. Elsewhere, I have tried to separate sentences and phrases to make it easier to read. Spellings are reproduced as they were written, sometimes with the same word spelt two or three different ways on the same page. Where I think it is helpful, I have put the correct spelling or missing letters in square brackets.

The book at first appears to date from the mid-18th century. There are inscriptions in the inside of the cover, giving the name Thomas Slapp and a date of 1764. This is probably not the author, but may be his son or grandson. The handwriting is different from that used in the book and the cover may not even be the original.

The text is very similar to that which appears in cures published during the plague years of 1636 and 1665. Many of the recipes mirror those in a book of entitled 'The Closet of Sir Kenelm Digby', written in the mid-seventeenth century. Though the writing is remarkably easy to read, two of the remedies described refer to a Doctor Hinton and a Dr. Buckworth, known as herbalists in in the mid-to-late seventeenth century.

The author may well be named Slapp. This is a name associated with Norfolk or northern Suffolk. (Relatively well-off Slapps have been traced to Sheringham, Overstrand and Trimmingham on the Norfolk coast as well as Rickinghall and Botesdale on the Suffolk side of the border with Norfolk). Add to this the fact that one recipe deals with samphire, a plant of East Anglian coastal marshes, and we may be a little nearer to discovering the book's origins. Today, a number of businesses in Norwich bear the name Slapp.

I have altered the order of the original document which begins and ends with preserves and recipes. As the most significant part of the book is dedicated to medical matters, I have started by putting those together. Otherwise, the text is exactly as transcribed.

Occasionally, the names of significant writers in this field will be mentioned; especially that of Thomas Culpeper (1616-1654), generally acknowledged as the father of modern herbalism.

Neither authors nor publishers endorse the safety or efficacy of any of the remedies or recipes described here. This is purely a work of historical reference, and we would strictly advise you not to try any of this at home.

Should you wish to understand more about herbal medicine, contact the National Institute of Herbalists at www.NIMH.com.

for the Rhume that offendeth the Eies

Take the purest Sallett oyle you can gett with mixture spread it like butter upon a toste of fine white bread and eat nothing for two or three hours after do this nine dayes it will help and worke a great effect in your body besides

for the Stone

Take the iuce of Elicampany and give it the party

Medical matters

into your mouth and it will cure you

A Remedy for the piles or Emrods Warrantable for ever

Take halfe a pinte of Lintseed oyle halfe an ounce of Vennice turpentine as much Verdigrease as will blend it into a high couler like starch, you temper all this together stir it untill it be cold, put it into a glass and keep it for your use make a tuft of lint as brode as a twenty shilling peice dip it in the oyle and apply it unto the greif if

For paines in the stomack or inward parts

Take a gallon of strong Ale and boile it in two handfull of Sentuary
a handfull of Rue untill halfe be consumed
then put in threequarters of a pound of browne Sugarcandy and let
it stand till the Sugarcandy be disolved on the fire.
drink of it every morning: fasting a good halfe pinte
this is good for ould [old] coughs

For the Gonorea

Take Venice Turpentine
wash it divers times in water till it look white
And put as much yolk of an egg as there is Turpentine
beat them well together
then stir it well into a small draught of a
white wine posset
so take it a morning fasting

For the Siatica

Ragwort boyled in hoggs grease till the ju[i]ce
be consumed
straine it then put in a little Mastick and
olibanum   and so make a plaster of it

Ragwort

~~~~~~~~~~~~~~~~~~~~~~~~~~~

'Sentuary' probably refers to the Common Centaury *(Centaurium umbellatum* or *Centaurium erythraea)*, though Culpepper refers to 'small centaury' in his own preparations. Rue or Herb of grace *(Ruta graveolens)* was a herb used with caution as it was known to cause a miscarriage.
Venice Turpentine was a resin produced from the European Larch. Other turpentines came from other members of the pine family.
A wine posset was a spiced drink of hot sweetened milk curdled with wine or ale.
Mastic is a resin obtained from a small evergreen tree of the Mediterranean, *(Pistacia lentiscus)*. Olibanum is a gum resin; a form of frankincense.

For the Dropsey or Green Sickness

Munks Ruborb halfe a pound
red mater [madder] roots halfe a pound
Seena [senna] foure ounces,
Anyseeds and Liquorish of each two ounces
Scabias [scabious] and Egrimony [Agrimony] of each two good
handfull   bruise them or steep them in ale or beere three dayes
and drink it three weeks together in the morning fasting & at four
of the clock in the afternoon

For a Corne

Take a little spung [sponge?]   steep it in Vinigar and put it in
halfe a nuttshell and lay it to the corn and it will weare it away

For an Eie with a thorn or bruise

Take two or three straines of the cock in a new laid egg
beat with some white sugarcandy.
finely beaten till it spread like a salve
then lay it on a cloth and binde it close to your eye

~~~~~~~~~~~~~~~~~~~~~~~~~~~~

Monks Rhubarb *(Rumex alpinus)* is a type of Dock. The root of Red Madder *(Rubia tinctorium)* was once an important source of dye. Senna is obtained from the pods of *Cassia augustifolia* or *acutifolia*. 'Straines of the cock' we take to mean the portion from which the embryo is to develop.

Field scabious

Dried herbs at Kentwell Hall

An approved Application for the spleen Gout or any ach[e] whatsoever by Mr Beelie

Take some Burgandy pitch and spread it upon a soft peece of
sheepskin as broad as you intend the plaster
warme the knife still and spread as quick as you can for it cooles
straight and then it will not spread well
when you have spread the seare cloth all over then spread it all over
with oxicroceum very thin in like manner as you did before with
burgandy pitch
prick it full of little holes
clap it too warme and let it stick till it come off

For Sore Eies [eyes]

Take an ounce of Lapis Calaminaris
an ounce of tuttia of Alexandria
burnt and quench them in white wine
nine times
then grinde them with capons grease

For the stinging of an Adder

Take garlick and fry it in oyle or may
butter or any other butter that hath no
salt in it but may butter is the best
lay it to the place stinged

Wild Garlic

~~~~~~~~~~~~~~~~~~~~~~~~~~~~~

Oxicroceum may refer to the Saffron Crocus, used in a number of herbal remedies, or
Meadow Saffron which was especially good for gout. Dried and powdered seeds and
corm produce the drug 'Colchicine'.
Lapis Calaminaris = hydrous silicate of zinc (Webster's Dictionary)
'Tuttia of Alexandria' = zinc carbonate.

For the Rhume that offendeth the Eies

Take the purest Sallett [salad] oyle you can gett without mixture
spread it like butter upon a toste of a fine white bread and eat
nothing for two or three hours after
do this nine dayes
it will help and worke a great effect in your body besides

For the Stone

Take the juce of Elicampany and give it to the party to drink
evening and morning in a little white wine.
it will certainly break the stone and help you

A Remedy for the piles or Emrods
Warrantable for ever

Take halfe a pinte of Lintseed oyle
halfe an ounce of Vennice turpentine
as much Verdigrease [verdigris] as will blend it into a high couler
like starch
temper all this together
stir it untill it be cold
put it into a glass and keep it for your use
make a tuft of lint as brode as a twenty shilling peice
dip it in the oyle and apply it unto the greif
if the greif be inward put a Violet comfit in the lint and dip it in
the oyle and put it up into the body

~~~~~~~~~~~~~~~~~~~~~~~~~~~~~~~

'Elicampany' is Elecampane *(Inula helenium)*, a large bright yellow flower used in
diseases of the chest & lungs.
Emrods can refer to haemorrhoids, piles, boils or tumours.
Verdigris is copper carbonate or (in sea air) copper chloride.
We take a violet comfit to be similar to a parma violet sweet.

Centaury

A very good water against any paine in the side the Loynes the brest and heart and it avoideth all distempers

Take a good handfull of Sentewary bruised and put into six pennyworth of Ale   then distill it   then put to it three ounces of Ginger sliced.   of Annyseeds & parsley seeds of each three ounces bruised   and let them steep in the water twenty foure hours and then distill it againe

For a sore mouth in old or young

Take the powder of Sage   the powder of allum [alum]   and temper it with good live honey drop it into your mouth and it will cure you

To cure the Syatica [sciatica]

Take a pound of good black sope [soap]
one pinte of good Aquavite   halfe a pinte of salit oyle
a quarter of a pint of the juce of Rue
boile them and stir them alltogether on an easie fire untill it be somthing thick
and if it may be made in a plaster then spread some thereof upon a peice of leather and apply it to the pained place
let it lye thereto unremoved three dayes and three nights and if the paine be not gon then apply such another plaster thereto and remove it not of so long and it will help it certainly

~~~~~~~~~~~~~~~~~~~~~~~~~~~~~

Alum refers to Potassium aluminium sulphate, used widely to reduce bleeding and to draw skin together. 'Aquavite' (aquavitae) is either alcohol or an alcoholic sprit such as brandy.   For 'Sentuary,' and Rue, see page 9.

A Plaster for any Ach Gout or Syatica
or to draw a thorne

Take stone pitch three ounces and a halfe
Rozin three ounces and a halfe
Littarage of Gold & Silver together of equal proportion one ounce
and a half   of bees wax three ounces and a dram,
of course turpentine three ounces
first melt the pitch wax and Rozin
then take it of the fire into a coole place and put in the
turpentine then the littarage being calcined into powder dust
stir them well together then power [pour] them out into a paile of
cold water and work it in and out with your
hands anoynted with oyle
and make it in small Rolls
you may make this receit [recipe] for ten pence

An Oyntment for the piles

Take three handfull of Elder leaves
one handfull of violet leaves a few Rosemary
topps   one handfull of summer savory
three heads of house leek   three leaves of orpin
stamp stamp them all in a morter and boyle it in
two pound of fresh butter
straine it very hot through through a strainer
then putt into it a quarter of a pound of

Orpine

unwrought bees wax and let it bee slowly boyled againe and cleane
scumed and so straine it againe   make it [in] may and keep it

~ ~

'Rozin' = rosin, the hard resin produced from certain pine trees
Summer savory - my dictionary refers to *Satureia hortensis* whose leaves were used
for seasoning.   House leek - see page 43
'Orpin' refers to Orpine *(Sedum telephium)*, also known as 'livelong'.

For the coming downe of the Fundament

Take a quart of white wine   a handfull of redd nettles
chop them and boyle them to a pinte
straine it and give it to the party to drink fasting in a morning or
before supper three spoonfull warmed
keep the herbs cleane and heat them and lay them on a cloth and
put up the place greeved with them

For the Flux

Take a pottle [a 2 quart drinking vessel] of new milk
foure ounces of oaken bark from the Tanner the out side shaved off
two ouncs of Cinomon both being broken in peices
boyle it slowley in the milk to three pintes or less   let the party
drink it as hot as they can a pottinger full night and morning

A Black Salve for a Boyle or bruised sore

Take Smellage Sallendine unset isop of each a handfull of dry
Cammomile flowers a pound   of spike one ounce
Bores grease Mutton suett halfe a pound of each
bruise them together and let them stand three dayes
then take halfe a pound of stone pitch
boyle all together till it fome [foams] and straine it and put in two
spoonfull of the oyle of roses

~~~~~~~~~~~~~~~~~~~~~~~~~~~~~~~

The Fundament generally refers to the area around the anus but may here mean some
kind of prolapse.   The Flux tended to mean dysentery or violent diarrhoea.
Inner oak bark, when boiled, yielded Tannic acid.
'Smellage' = Smallage or wild celery *(Apium graveolens)* or may be Lovage
(Levisticum officinale)
'Sallendine' = Celandine *(Ranunculus majus* or *Chelidonium majus)*
'Spike' may refer to Spike Lavender *(Lavendula angustifolia {spica officinalis})* or
Spikenard *(Arelia racemosa),* though the latter tends to be used internally.
'Isop' = Hyssop *(Hyssopus officinalis),* an aromatic plant.

An Excellent water for a sore eye or green wound or for a Canker

Take plantine leaves the flowers and leaves of woodbine the youngest tops of fenill eybright herbigrace Sallendine Sage Poliknot grass tapson Agremonie and Marygold leaves of each halfe a handfull and boile them together in a pottle of runing water till halfe the water be consumed then straine out the water from the hearbs setting the decocktion againe upon the fire putting thereto three ounces of roch Allome and six spoonfull of pure honey & let it boile againe till a quarter be consumed then put it into a viall and keep it for your use

To make Flos Unguentorum

Take rozen and burgandie pitch of each halfe a pound of Virgins wax Frankinsence of each a quarter of a pound of Mastick one ounce of harts tallow a quarter of a pound Camphire two dram melt all that is to be melted and powder all that is to be powdered and cearce it finely then boyle them over the fire and straine them through a canvas cloth into a pottle of white wine then boile the wine with all the other ingredience together it must boile till the wine be consumed and let it coole till it be no hotter then blood

For a Purge

Take the weight of two shillings of Ruburb and put thereto twelve spoonfulls of white wine and six spoonfulls of Suckerye or endif [endive] water and sum twenty reasons [raisins] of the Sunn stoned and one spoonfull of Anniceeds bruised
infuse all these together one night in a pott close stopped upon embers and the next day straine it out very hard and take it putting a little sugar thereto

Goodwife Fosters Salve for all sores

Take a pennyworth of Vennice Turpentine
a spoonfull of life honey
a spoonfull of Gaults grease
halfe a spoonfull of the juce of selfe heale
as much Rozen as an egg
as much or rather more of bees wax
if you will have it to eat out dead or proud
flesh then putt in as much white coppris
as a hazel nut
boyle all these on a soft fire as long as it will rise

Self-heal

then keep it in an earthen pott for your use

~~~~~~~~~~~~~~~~

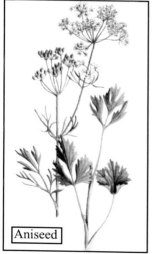

Aniseed

Suckery and endive are both alternative names for chicory *(Cichorium intybus)*.
'Life' [live] honey is probably runny honey.
Gault's grease may be goose grease.
'Selfe heale' *(Prunella vulgaris)*, as the name suggests, was well known for its medicinal properties.
Coppris was another name for Green Flax *(Grana germanica)*. The plant known as Goldthread *(Coptis chinensis)* is another possibility. However, this does sound more chemical than botanic; Ferrous Sulphate was known as Copperas, though it was green in colour.

An Excellent water for a sore eye or a green wound or for a Canker

Take plantine leaves   the flowers and leaves of woodbine
the youngest tops of fennill eyebright herbigrace Sallendine Sage
Poliknot grass tapson Agremonie and Marygold leaves of each
halfe a handfull and boile them to gether in a pottle of runing
water till halfe the water be consumed
the[n] straine out the water from the hearbs setting the decocktion
againe upon the fire putting thereto three ounces of roch Allome and
six spoonfull of pure honey & let it boile againe till a quarter be
consumed   then put it into a viall and keep it for your use

To make Flos Unguentorum

Take rozen and burgandie pitch of each halfe a pound
of Virgins wax   Frankinsence of each a quarter of a pound
of Mastick one ounce
of Harts tallow a quarter of a pound   Camphire two drams
melt all that is to be melted and powder all that is to be powdered
and cearce it finely
then boyle them over the fire and straine them through a
canvas cloth into a pottle of white wine
then boile the wine with all the other ingredience together
it must boile till the wine be consumed and let it coole till it be no
hotter then [than] blood
then put thereto a quarter of a pound of turpentine ever
stirring it till it be thorow [thoroughly] cold
but ever beware that your stuff be not hotter then [than] blood
when you put in the turpentine and camphire for if it be it spoileth
all your stuff
then when it is cold make it up in roles [rolls] and keep it for your
use for it is the best and most preciouest salve that can be made.
that is called the flower for all wounds.

it is cleansing and gendereth good flesh

And it healeth more in a Sennigh[t] then [than] any other in a month

it suffereth no corruption in a wound nor no ill flesh to be gendered

it is good for the head ach[e] and singing in the braine and for all manner of impostunes in the head or body for blowing in the eares or cheeks for Sinnues [sinews? sinuses?] sprongs [sprains].

it draweth out any thorne or any broken bones or anything that is in a wound

it is good for any bighting or stinging of any venomous beast

it rotteth and healeth all manner of botchs.

it is good for a sefter canker And it draweth all manner of aches out of the spleen or raines it breaketh the impostune

it is good for the routing in the members

it is good to cease the flux of menstness [menstruation] if it be lait with a plaster to a Womans navill and healeth faire the Emrolds

And is speciall good to make seare cloths for the gout and aches pestilence and botchis

~~~~~~~~~~~~~~~~~~~~~~~

'Plantine' = Great Plantain *(Plantago major)*;

Woodbine = Honeysuckle *(Lonicera periclymenum)*; 'Fennill' = Fennell *(Foeniculum vulgare)*; Eyebright *(Euphrasia officinalis)*, as the name suggests was used widely for complaints of the eye. Herbigrace is another name for Rue.

Poliknot grass was probably Knotweed *(Polygonum aviculare)*. The meaning of 'Tapson' is questionable, though Agrimony and Marigold are familiar enough.

Alum is mentioned on page 13, though this may mean a slightly different form.

Flos Ungentorum or 'flower of all wounds' appears in a number of collections of herbal treatments, having a wide variety of applications.

Virgins wax refers to unused beeswax. Hart's tallow was hard fat made from the bones of deer.

'Camphire' = Camphor, a product of a far-eastern tree related to cinnamon. Crystals of camphor oil occur in the wood and have long been used in rheumatic treatments, cough mixtures and ointments. The 'Camphor plant' or Alecost *(Tanacetum balsamita)* was grown in England as an aromatic alternative.

Several words on this page gave us difficulty with their precise definition, though their context makes them fairly clear - e.g. botchs (swellings or pimples), sefter (canker, abcess or ulcer), raines (urinary tract), impostune, routing.

Melilot

Betony

Chamomile

For the Spleene Plaster

Take Mellelot and Cammomile of each a handfull
Roman Wormwood and parsley Plantine and Bettane of each a
handfull beat them small in a stone morter
putt in three pound of fine Rozin twelve Ounces of Sheeps suett
a pinte of white wine
melt them together in an earthen pott
let stand eight dayes then boile them perfectly
straine and keep it for your use

An Excellent oyle for an ach[e]

Take as many snailes as you can get such as have shells
putt them into a bagg and fill the bagg with salt.
knit the bagg fast and hang it up and set under it a pewter dish to
receive that which dropeth out of the bagg and keep it to annoynt
any part of a mans body where he feeleth any ach[e]
an Excellent oyle approved by the Lord Morrice and divers others

~~~~~~~~~~~~~~~~~~~~~~~~~~~~~~~~~

Roman Wormwood *(Artemisia pontica)*, a non-native wormwood in this country.
'Bettane' = Betony *(Stachys betonica)*.
Slapp uses a variety of different mortars for different purposes, and a wide variety of
storage pots and jars. He is quite specific over which are to be used in each case.

An Electuary for any cough excellent good ap[p]roved by L John Pate

Take two ounces of Alicompane two ounces of Liquorish
two ounces of Annyseeds two ounces of orris roots
and two oun[c]es of browne sugar candy
dry these very well and beat them to powder and cleare them and
mingle it with life honey and every morning take the quantaty of a
Walnut and fast after it two hours and you may take as much last
at night when you go to bed

To help Diseases to expell winde and Strengthen the Stomack

Take half a pound of Marmolet [marmalade] of
quinces
six oun[c]es of the best red Vinigar

Quince

bruise the Marmolet with the Vinigar till it have no lumps
then worke with it two ounces of white sugar small beaten
And when they are mixed well together sett them on a soft fire
let them boyle leasurely to allmoste the thickness of conserv[e]
then take it of[f] the fire and put in these spices
put white pepper long pepper and black peper of each of them an
ounce: of ginger a quarter of an ounce   one nutmeg
Diabra two drams   stir it till it be cold
take halfe an hour after you meat [eat?] the bigness of a great
nutmeg.   it will not onely help disseases but expell winde and
streangthen the stomack

~~~~~~~~~~~~~~~~

An electuary was a drug mixed with sugar and water or honey (Universal Dictionary)
Alicompane' = Elecampane - see page 10.
Orris roots (Iris florentina), the wild purple flag, a non-native plant.
For 'life' or 'live' honey, read 'runny honey.'   Diabra may just be *Bebe diabara*,
a South American Broom renowned for its medicinal qualities.

For the Back

Take yellow Amber one ounce,   shavings of ivory one ounce;
red Corrall one dram.   prepared pearle one dram,
red Saunders halfe a dram;   Mastick one dram,
boyle one dram Terra Siggalata.
one ounce date stones   halfe an ounce Cinamon
one ounce dried turpentine
beat all these to a fine powder and drink it
[in] wine or Beare [beer] morning and
evening what quantity you please

For sore Eies

Ale hoofe Celendine and daisie leaves stamped
and strained   put to it rose water and sugar
drop it with a feather into the eie

To make Jelly for a Consumption

Take two Ounces of shaved harts horne
half a pinte of white wine
a pinte and a halfe of spring water
stew it close covered till it be consumed
then straine it and put in a stick or two of Cinomon a race of
ginger   A little sweet Marjeram   and let it stand all night
then season it with a little sugar halfe a spoonfull of redd rose water
a sprig of rosemary and juce of Orange & leamon [lemon] and take
out the spice   let it stew covered a little time
take three spoonfull warme in a morning

Ground Ivy

~~~~~~~~~~~~~~~~~~~~~~~~

Red Saunders is likely to be Red Sandalwood (also called Sanders Wood) -
(Pterocarpus Santalinus).
'Terra Siggalata' is a clay-like suspension, used today as a slip applied to pottery.
'Ale hoofe' is another name for Ground Ivy *(Glechoma hederacea)*.

For an inward Bruse

Take the juce of the leaves or Roots of Solomans
seale in Ale or white wine and drink a reasonable
quantaty
it helpeth speedily and being stamped and laid
to bruses or broken bones of a man or beast it
healpeth   this drink is good for man or beast

Solomon's Seal

An Excellent Medicine for all burns or Scaldings

Take ground Ivye alehoofe dasie leaves and roots of each a handfull
mince them with as much Deare suit [deer suet] or sheeps suit as
will fry them all together and take heed they burn not & so straine
them and annoint the place with it being warmed
but let no linnen cloath [cloth] touch it unless it be fine lawn or a
bladder   your salve will keep good this seaven yeares
the best way is to boyle them in a quart of creame to oyle them
put halfe a pound of suet to it and so straine it and use it warme

For a Stich

Wheat beaten and boyled in mace ale and eat it warme and ley to
swet

A Cold for a Horse

Take Aniseeds and Liquorish   dry them by the fire then beat them
to powder   then work them to a paste with fresh butter
then hallow with your finger.
after it is rouled up like an egg then fill the hallow full of tar and
so give it to your Horse in the morning
then ride him untill he sweat   then bring him into the stable
and cloth him warme and let him stand

For the yallow Jandis

Take the yallow barke of a barbery tree & beat it to powder and
take as much as wil ley on threepence in a spoonfull of beare [beer]
in the morning fasting four or five dayes

For a Bile to break and heal

Take a little creame and a little seared oatmeale and mix it thick
and lay it on
dress it morning and evening.
probatum [proven]

For the Paine of the Piles

Take a great onion
core it and fill it with butter or oyle and rost [roast] it in embers till
it be soft
binde it to the place

For sore Eies [eyes]

Take an ounce of Lapis Calaminaris
an ounce of Tutia of Alexandria
burn and quench them in white wine nine times
then grind them with capons grease

To recover the eies sight

Take Smalledg Fennell Rew Vermin Egrimony Bittony Scabious
Avens Houstung [hound's tongue] a hearb [herb] so called ufrage
Pimpernell and sage
still this in a mans childs urin[e] with five grains of
frankinsence
drop this in the eyes when you go to bed

For the Piles

Take Mallows Avens Ladys mantle
boile them in flat milk till they be very tender
then bath the place warme with it and then lay some of the hearbs
as warme as you can suffer it to the place and it will aswage
[assuage] and heale it.

A Receipt for Convultion fits which cured Mrs Miles of Hertfordshire who was trobled with them 20 yeares

Take an ounce of white piony Roots dried and beaten to powder
halfe an ounce of coriander seeds   halfe an ounce of piony seeds
halfe an ounce of Rosemary tops dried and beaten to powder
mix these all together and take as much as will lie on six pence in
some three or four spoonfulls of black cherry water warmed
drink it morning and evening three dayes before the full of the
moone and three dayes after

~~~~~~~~~~~~~~~~~~~~~~~~~~~~

Barberry tree *(Berberis vulgaris)* has a bright yellow coloured bark.
Lapis Calaminaris & 'Tutia of Alexandria' (see page 11)
'Smalledg' = Smallage (Lovage or Wild Celery) *(Levisticum officinale)* ;
'Rew' = Rue (see page 9); 'Vermin' may mean Vervain. It might be a form of
wormwood, which is used as a vermifuge and also in the
making of vermouth. 'Egrimony' = Agrimony (see page 10).
'Bittony' = Betony *(Stachys betonica)*.
'Avens' refers to Herb Bennet.
(Geum urbanum).   Pimpernell is easily recognised, but
'ufrage' remains a bit of a mystery. It seems to describe a
form of Pimpernell. Scarlet Pimpernell was once used as a
folk remedy, but possibly our plant is the Yellow Loosestrife,
formerly called the Wood Pimpernell and reputed to help the
eyesight (according to Culpeper). However, more likely, it is
Burnet Saxifrage *(Pimpinella saxifraga)*.
Lady's Mantle *(Alchemilla vulgaris)*, was renowned for
stopping bleeding and healing all manner of wounds.

Lady's Mantle

For those that are subject to faint sweats

Take Sowthistle   Soothernwood Endive the hearb Mercury and
night shade of each a handfull
boile them in two quarts of water untill halfe be consumed
straine it and put to the straining white wine vinigar untill it be
sowrish and then put sugar into it untill it be sweetish
drink of this warme before you go to bed or when your sweating fit
cometh

For the stoping of the stomack or a cold

Take the powder of Elicampane the powder of Sulpher and the
powder of liquorish each a like quantity
mix them together and make them into pills with English honey
take of them three or foure spoonfull in a morning fasting
fast two hours and stir moderatly after them

For the stone in the kidney or bladder

Take two pound of Althea roots   wash them cleane and scrape them
and pound them in a stone morter
take one ounce of parsley seed and three ounces of Anyseeds
bruise them in a morter
take one pound of white and red yarrow the leaves and flowers on it
put all these together and steep them twenty foure hours in two
quarts of right white wine
add thereto two quarts of new milk and halfe an ounce of white rose
leaves or halfe an ounce of white rose water
put them all together into a still and still them as fast as you can
this water is not to be drunk till six weeks after it is stilled but keep
it close stopped in glass bottles and then you may drink a quarter of
a pinte in a morning seasoned with sugar as often as you please
And if you sometimes put in it the juce of Leamon it will be much
the better for it.

For one in danger of miscarrying or a weak Back

Take nine or tenn treadles out of eggs a spoonfull of Sugar candy
a spoonfull or two of rose water
as much Boalarmonick as will lie upon a shilling
mix these together and swallow it
take it three mornings together and it will cure you & make you
strong

To kill wormes in the Body

Take fearne Roots made into fine powder one dram which being
dissolved in white wine give the patient to drink and it will kill
them all.

~~~~~~~~~~~~~~~~~~~~~~~~

The Common Sowthistle *(Sonchus oleraceus)* or Corn (or Tree) Sowthistle
(S. arvensis).

So[u]thernwood *(Artemisia abrotanum)*, is an aromatic shrub with a variety of uses.

The herb then known as (English) Mercury is what gardeners today call 'Fat-Hen' or
'Good King Henry' *(Chenopodiumbonus-henricus)*. Alternatively, this may be French
Mercury *(Mercurialis annua)*

Deadly Nightshade *(Atropa belladonna)*: the berries
are poisonous, but the leaves and roots can be used
for external applications.

'Elicampane' = Elecampane (see page 12)

'Sulpher' = sulphur

'Liquorish' = liquorice root, *(Glycyrrhiza glabra)*
is one of the most common ingredients in this book.

'Althea' = Marshmallow *(Althea officinalis)*

Yarrow *(Achillea millefolium)*.

'Boalarmonick' remains a bit of a mystery, though
the 'treadles of eggs' are presumably what he
describes on page 10 as 'straines of the cock'.

'Fearne roots' are most likely to come from what is
often called the Male Fern *(Dryopteris filix-mas)*

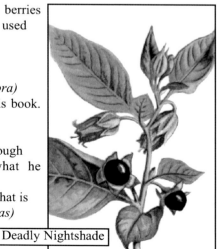

Deadly Nightshade

To make one sleep that is light in the head

Take greene moss that groweth on the ground and when it is dry
boyle it in posset drink made with white wine
sweeten it with sugar and drink it when you go to bed

For giddiness in the head

Take conserve of Bettony and conserve of pioney of each an equall
quantity
mix them together and take as much as a nutmeg in the morning
fasting at foure of the clock in the after noon and at night when
you go to bed.

A very good water Against paine in the side the Loynes the brest and Heart and it Avoideth all Infermities

Take a good handfull of Sentewary bruised and put into six penny
worth of Ale   then disstill it   then put to it three ounces of Ginger
sliced of Annyseeds and parsley
seeds of each three ounces bruised
and let them steep in the water
twenty foure hours
and the[n] disstill it againe

In the stillroom at Kentwell Hall, Suffolk

~~~~~~~~~~~~

'Bettony' = Betony *(Stachys betonica)*. This
plant is also classified as *Betonica officinalis*
& *Stachys officinalis*.
'Pioney' = Paeony *(Paeonia officinalis)* is
given a variety of spellings in this book. The
conserve would be made from the roots.
A host of superstitions existed concerning this
plant.
'Sentewary' = Centaury (see page 9)

A Remedy for the Palsie in the Head

Take the gum of ive [ivy] as much as two pease and worke it every night in palmes of your hands untill you have wrought it in for tenn nights together
And by Gods help it shall cure you

A Remedy for the winde Collick when all other Remidies faile

Take a beare glass full of running water
drink thereof cold
if it help not in an hours space drink another

To bring the stone away that lieth in the bladder or the kidneys

Take halfe a pinte of Sack as much white wine as much stale beare [beer] and as much clarrett [claret] wine
take one quarter of a pound of setwell roots sliced and lay them in steep twelve hours with the ju[i]ce of a leamon [lemon]
power [pour] forth a draught at a time and make it pleasant with sirrup [syrup] of marshmallous and drink it when ocation [occasion] serves
this will cure all inward gravell and void it with ease so as you shall have no paine but be cured at pleasure

~~~~~~~~~~~~~~~~~~~~

'Setwell' roots are the roots of Valerian, also known as 'Setwall' and 'All-Heal' *(Valeriana officinalis)*. Like many others used in this book, this plant has a wide range of medicinal uses. According to Culpeper, marshmallow syrup made the passages slippery, so enabling the body to void stones.

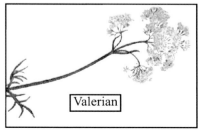

Valerian

An Excellent Remedy for a Rupture

Take Ackorne boules stems and all and dry them in an Oven one
ounce beaten to powder
as much of the thinest Synomon [cinnamon]
take a quarter of an ounce of each at a time in a posett drink or
broth three dayes together in the morning in March if you can.
first the boules must be beaten very small then the Synomom
and then both together
then put up your body and leggs not straining them by any meanes
then at the change of the moon in the same moneth if you take a
pinte of milk a quarter of an ounce of Synomon beaten very small
and two spoonfull of beane flower   boyle all together very well
take one halfe in the morning   the other at night when you go to
bed three dayes before the new moone and three dayes after
be sure to beate the Synoman very well

An excellent water for the Eyes

Take two ounces of the best and clearest Myrrh which must be
pulvered and put to a quart of canary sack in which it must steep
all night ⊕ distill it the next morning in a glass still,
when it is drawn of it will be as cleare as runing water
keep it two months that the fire may be out before it is used
And then with a fine cloth diped therein wash the eyes open every
morning or drop a little into the corner of the eyes when they are
painfull   And continue so doing as long as there is cause
this is aproved a great preserver of the eyes

~~~~~~~~~~~~~~~~~~~~

'Ackorne boules' are oak galls or oak apples.
'Posett drink' - see page 9
'Canary sack' was strong white wine imported from The Canaries.
Myrrh (Commiphora molmol) - an oleo-gum-resin from the stem, rarely used the way
Slapp suggests.

A water for the winde

Take one quart of Spirrit of wine
put therein one pound of Carroway cumfits
stop it close and let the glass be shaked every day untill the sugar be
wasted from the seeds
then keep it for your use
and it is one of the best things for the winde that can be

An Excellent Remedy for the winde
in the Stomack in the gutts in the Bladder
or to make water freely

Take a quart of Ale possett drink one pennyworth of parsley seeds
as much fennell seeds as much of nettle seeds
boyle all these together a quarter of an hour then take it from the
fire and put halfe a pinte of white wine into it and a
quarter of a pound of sugar
then sett it on the fire againe and let it boyle a while
then straine it and put it into a bottle and drink it when
ocation serveth milk warme

For one that is subject to miscarrej

Take the juce of plaine a little sugar candy and Corrall
two spoonfulls at a time and it will help with Gods leave

~~~~~~~~~~~~~~~~~~~~~~~~~

'Carroway cumfits' - Culpeper describes these as 'confects', meaning sweets made
from Caraway seeds dipped in sugar which 'is a most admirable remedy for those
that are troubled with wind.'
'Plaine' may mean some concoction from the Plane tree, but is more likely to be a
juice produced from the Plantain *(Plantago major)* - see page 19.
Coral may mean ground-up coral, but probably refers to Crawley Root, otherwise
called Coral Root *(Corallorhiza odontorhiza)*.

A drink to bring forth the small pox purples or Measles

Make posset Ale
take the curd of[f] and boyle one handfull of red Fennell
when it is well [done] straine it
And put thereto the quantity of a nutmeg of fine treacle setwell
and english safforn [saffron?]
being all mixed together give it the patient to drinke warme

For a sore mouth in old or young

Take the powder of Sage the powder of Allum and temper it with
good live honey
drop it into your mouth and it will cure you Approved

An Electuary for the sickness to take in the morning before you go abroade

Take an ounce of London Treacle a quarter of a pound of Sugar
the juce of a handfull of earbagrace one pennyworth of white wine
vinigar   put these in a puter [pewter] dish over a chafeing dish of
coales stirring them together untill it comes to the body of an
Electuary   then put it into a gally pott and take the quantity of a
nutmeg in the morning fasting as long as it lasteth and walk after
this is aproved

~~~~~~~~~~~~~~~~~~~~~~~~~~~

'Purples' probably refers to *Purpura Haemorrhagica*, or Purple disease which causes
discolouring of the skin.
'Posset ale' was made by curdling spiced sweetened milk with ale.
True Saffron would have been imported, and was very expensive.
Culpepper describes it as a cure for pestilence, smallpox & measles.
English Meadow Saffron *(Colchicum autumnale)*, which seems to be referred to here
is more renowned for helping with gout & rheumatism.
An electuary could be a very thick cordial syrup. 'Earbagrace' = Rue (see page 9)

For an Ague

Take three Ounces Barley water
one handfull of hearb Avins
halfe a handfull of plantine
boyle these together till it come to halfe a pinte
then straine it and put into the juce a quarter
of a pinte of white wine and drink it an hour
before the fit come and stir after it a while
and then ley downe warme
if it drive it not away at once do it the next fit

Herb Bennet (Avens)

For the wood evell in sheep

Take of Fetherfew wornwood Lavender cotton Rewe white dasie
roots of each a handfull   stamp and straine them with verjuce
then put therein of Turmarick and Safforn beaten of each a
pennyworth   and put all into a poot or bottle
put thereof into every nostrill of the sheep one spoonfull and two
into the mouth

To kill a Fellon

Take the ouldest Bacon you can get and unsett leeks and bray them
together & let it be made plaster wise and lay it on your desease

~~~~~~~~~~~~~~~~~~~~~~~~~~~~

'Avins' = Avens (see pages 24 & 25) 'Plantine' = Plantain (see pages 19 & 31)
'Fetherfew' = Feverfew *(Tanacetum parthenium)*.
'Wornwood' = Wormwood (see page 20) This may, however, be the native
wormwood *(Artemisia absinthium),* also known as Green Ginger.
Cotton Lavender *(Chamaecyparissus santolina).*   'Rewe' = Rue (see page 9)
'White dasie' may mean the Common Daisy *(Bellis perenis)* or possibly the Ox-eye
daisy *(Leucanthemum vulgare).*
'Verjuce' could mean Vermouth (which contained extract of wormwood)
'Turmarick' = Turmeric, the powdered rhizome of *Curcuma longa.*
A 'fellon' was a whitlow on the finger.

For the Rickets

Take two ounces of Liquorish as much annyseeds and one pound
of Reasons of the sunn [raisins] stoned three large handfulls of
_____ [torn page] three of motherwort three of harts to____
[torn page] boyle all these in two gallons of spring water untill
halfe be consumed   so straine and let the party drink no other
drink

My Lady Delafountaines strengthening Pills

Take the jaw bone of a pike dried and beaten to powder

then take venis turpentine
of the bigness of a nutmeg
steep it all night in wine
vinigar being pricked full
of holes and drie it

Pike

make it in powder   mix it with the rest and role it in sugar
make pills and take three nine mornings together fasting
eat not for an hower [hour] after
the pills must be as big as a hazlenut

Mrs Adkinses Lossenges for a cold

Take an ounce of fine powder of Liquorish   foure ounces of sugar
wett it with isopp water so much as will desolve it and let it boyle
on the fire with continuall stirring till it be thick
drop into it foure or five drops of oyle of anniseed
then power it out and mould it like paste in ounce of the best flower
of brimstone and make it into little cakes as broade as twopence

~~~~~~~~~~~~~~~~~~~~~~~~~~~~~~

'Strengthening pills' is a bit of a euphemism - they were prescribed for impotence.
Motherwort *(Leonorus cardiaca)*. 'Harts to___' might mean Harts tongue, referred to
by Culpeper, a perennial fern *(Phyllitis scolopendrium)*.
'Issop' = Hyssop *(Hyssopus officinalis)* - see page 15.
'Flower of Brimstone' refers to 'flowers of sulphur'.

Doctor Hintons Cordiall Broth against Consumptions

Take knuckles of mutton and knuckles of Veale of each two handfulls
of Salsapella & of China: of each two ounces
of hartshorn and ivory. of each one ounce
of Raysons of the sunn stoned and of currants of pruns halfe a pound,
of sweet Marjoram Time and Balme of each halfe a handfull.
of Burrage and buglose flowers and of Archangel flowers and of cowslips of each a quarter of a hand full
boyle these things together in sixteene pintes of spring water unto eight pintes adding towards the latter end of the decoction
of conserve of woodsorrell   conserve of red roses
conserve of Gilliflowers   of each one ounce
straine it and drink it a good draught thereof three times a day blood warme
let it be boyled in an earthen pipkin

~~~~~~~~~~~~~~~~~~~~~~~~~~~

Lemon Balm

We have been unable to trace most of the people referred to in this book. Dr. Hinton does however feature as a seventeenth century herbalist.

'Salsapella' = Sarsparilla *(Smilax ornata)*.

'China' is probably *Smilax china*, a form of sarsparilla used by Culpeper.

'Time' = Thyme (many different varieties).

'Balme' = Lemon Balm *(Melissa officinalis)*.

'Burrage' = Borage *(Borago officinalis)*.

'Buglose' = Viper's Bugloss *(Echium Vulgare)*.

'Archangel' *(Lamium)* was the name given to all varieties of dead-nettle, red, white & yellow.

Wood Sorrel *(Oxalis acetosella)*.   Gilliflower was originally the name given to Pinks *(Dianthus)* but subsequently came to refer to a number of fragrant blooms such as Stocks and Wallflowers *(Cheranthus cheiri)*.

35

A plaster for all manner of aches approved by my old Lord of Exeter

Take stone pitch and pure Rozen of like quantity
a little virgins wax sheeps tallow double the quantity of the rest
and boile all upon a soft fire
then put into a bowle of faire water could la____ [torn page] with
your hands but not too much
then it will look yellow which is ve_____ [torn page]
then keep it for your use
when you use it melt thereof as much as much as needeth
put thereto powder of mace and comming seeds
spred it upon the rough side of a sheeps skin and lay it to the place
untill it come of[f] by its own accord
it is soveraigne medicine an[d] Approved

My Lady Harringtons Oyle for the spleen Collick or any paine in the stomack

Take Lavender Fennill Parsley Cammomil time sage
sothernwood Rosemary pellitory of the wall annyseeds
fennell seeds of each a handfull;
comming seeds two handfull
cloves two ounces mace one ounce
dry the hearbs in the sunn two dayes
then bruise the seeds and chop the herbs
and bruise the spice and put them into
a pot of sallet oyle
and set it in the sunn tenn dayes
then put into it halfe a pinte of oyle of bitter
Almonds and halfe a pinte of oyle of caper
and annoint the place agreeved warme
every morning and night probatum

Pellitory-of-the-wall

36

The Sympatheticall powder

Take of the best Roman Viteriall or fine transparent blew Viteriall
made out of copper mine

bruise it into fine powder and lay it in the Sun till it be white
which will be in two months or there abouts

be sure in the meane time least dust or raine spoyle it

if you will have it quicker made calcine it softly with a
burning glass so that it looke white and not yellow and keep this
powder for your use.

The use of it is to cure wounds where there is eyther blood or matter
you are to cause the wound to bleed or matter by jently
pressing it with your hand before you dress it

Then dip a cloth in the blood or matter and strow some of the
powder ther[e]on

wrap this cloth in another and keep it in a warme place or in your
pocket

if it be a great wound dress it twice or thrice after this manner
keep only the wound cleane and it will quickly be cured

A plaster for any soar or to take away pain

Take rosen wax oyl frankincence hogs lard of each a like quantity
boyle them together and straine them and use them as plasters

~~~~~~~~~~~~~~~~~~~~~~~~~~~~

Virgins wax (see pages 18 & 19)
'Comming seeds' = Cumin *(Cuminum cyminum)*.
'Fennill' = Fennel *(Foeniculum vulgare)*.
'Cammomil' = Chamomile *(Chamaemelum nobile)*.
'Sothernwood' = Southernwood *(Artemisia abrotanum)*.
Pellitory-of-the-wall *(Parietaria officinalis)*.
'Oyle of Caper' *(Capparis spinosa)* - the unripe buds of
the caper bush were used to produce the oil.
The word 'viteriall' is a bit of a mystery, but probably
means Zinc Sulphate (known as white vitriol) and
Copper Sulphate (known as blue vitriol).

Fennel

For a weaknes in the back

Take the white of an egg
beat it very well   then take as much mastick in fine powder as will
ly upon a sixpence
stur all together and drink it up & a glass of sack after it
take it early in the morning   ly in bed two hours after it

An Ey[e] water

Take halfe a peck of rye lof hot from the oven
put the crum into a still with all the speed you can haveing furst
put in two handfulls of ey bright and destill it of as fast as you can

To make an Ague oyntment

Take sothernwood red sage
wormwood rue fetherfew
cammomile inward bark of elder
and make them into an oyntment

For a straine or weakness in a lim[b]

Take oyle of venus turpentine sweet
oyle and brandy and worme [warm]
them together and bath[e] the place
very well against the fier [fire] and
lay flanell on the place

~~~~~~~~~~~~

'Mastick' - see page 9   Ey[e]bright - see pages 18 & 19
'So[u]thernwood' - see page 37   Wormwood - see pages 20 & 33
'Fetherfew' = Feverfew - see page 33   'Sack' - see page 30
'Venus' [Venice] turpentine - see page 9
Elder *(Sambucus nigra)* was used medicinally, but as the bark was being used here, it
is possibly the Dwarf Elder *(Sambucus ebulus)*.

A green oyntment to be made in May

it is good for stifness of the joynts shrinking of the sinnew or pain
in the stich in the side or of liver and spleen or ague
fallen into any part of the flesh if it be taken before it grows to an
imposter. for brusis and knots
it will also take away swelling or blackness.

Take two pound of deer suitt [suet] rew [rue] sage
wormwood feather few [feverfew] lavender green and cotten
plantine   of each a like quantaty
a good handfull of St John wort
beat them in a stone morter with the deere suit very small
then take neats foot oyle a pinte
then put all into an earthen pot and let it remaine a month
then boyle it straine it and keep it close for your use

~ ~ ~ ~ ~ ~ ~ ~ ~ ~ ~ ~ ~ ~ ~ ~

An 'imposter' presumably meant a wound that had
turned septic.
Two entirely different Lavenders are described here,
Cotton Lavender *(Santolina chamaecyparissus)*
and true lavender *(Lavendula augustifolia)*

With the latter, it was the aromatic flowers that were more commmonly used, but here he is suggesting using it green .

Neat's-foot oil was a light yellow oil produced from the feet and shin bones of cattle, used primarily for dressing leather.

St. John's Wort - also referred to on the next page as Apericon *(Hypericum perforatum)*

39

Lucatellas Balsom

Take one quart of sallet oyle 1s 06d
yellow wax halfe a pound
of venus turpentine one quarter of a pound 10d
liquid storax six ounces 1s 06d   oyle of Apericon halfe an ounce 2d
natural balsome halfe an ounce 1s 3d
rose water and plantane water of each 2d
red sanders halfe an ounce 6d
dragons blood halfe an ounce muming 4d
Rosemary baise [bay?] and sweet marjerom of each a handfull
balme a handfull

Thus it must be made

Take your Sallett Oyle and a pinte of faire water
boyle it with in an earthen pott in your wax
then shred the hearbs very small and put them and the sanders
and the rosemary and planting water into the pott and let it boyle
a little   then bruise the Dragons blood very small and putt them
in letting them boyle a little
then take the turpentine and wash it three times in faire water and
the last time in rose water
then putt it into the pott letting it boyle a little
then putt in the oyle of Apericon and the naturall Balsom
letting them all boyle halfe a quarter of an hour
then sett it to coole
And when it is cold put the water from it and melt it againe   if it
be foule at the bottome you may straine it then put it up you may
keep the watter that comes from it to wash sores

The virtues are these

For a cold take as much of it as a walnutt and melt it in a sawser
then power it into a penny worth of sack being warme and so drink
it going to bed annointing the temples and Stomack with a little of
it also

For a Burn or Scald

Take of it and Annoint it with a feather upon the burne or any green wound scald or wound or sore brest as hot as may be endured washing a womans brest first with the water of it

For an outward bruse or straine

Rub thereon against the fire a good while as hot as you can indure it laying a hot cloth thereon

take it in a penny pot of sack as aforesaid.

And it will part a woman and her child where there is much danger and very hard and long labour

it is good also for any kinde of inward bruise or extreame flux costiveness or for them that have swallowed pins or needles or any thing else that trobles

it is excellent against the consumption

And in general it is good against all aches and paines and swellings both inward and outward

it is good for them that have eaten and drunken poyson to be taken as aforesaid

dip black wool in some of it and putt into the eares and it healpe deafness

the sack must be warmed first and then the balsome must be melted by it self and so powered into the sack and drunk

~~~~~~~~~~~~~~~~~~~~~~~~

'Liquid storax' was a balsam obtained from the trunk of *Liquidamber orientalis.*
'Apericon' is probably St. John's Wort *(Hypericum perforatum)* -see page 39.
'Natural balsome' is probably *Tanacetum balsamita* - see page 19. It seems to be in resin form as at the end of the recipe it is to be melted.
'Red sanders' - see page 22.
'Dragons blood' is a rare plant *(Daemomorops draco)*: alternatively, this may refer to *Arisaema consanguineum,* often called the Dragon plant, used in Chinese medicine.
'Sallett oyle' [salad oil] - see page 12 - probably olive oil.
Extreme flux refers to bad diarrhoea; costiveness meaning constipation.
Consumption meant tuberculosis of the lungs, but also any disease that gave rise to the wasting of tissues; hence references to 'a consumption' (page 22) and [numbers of] consumptions (page 35).

To make Harts horne Jelly

Take halfe a pound of harts horn
wash it lightly in water
then put it to two quarts of spring water
set it on a gentell fire to simer
you may finde when it is enough by takeing a little in a spoone
and let it coole
And when you finde that it will jelly take the liquor and runn it
through a jelly bag
then put it into a cleane pan and set it over a quick fire till it boile
then take the juce of three or foure leamons and put it to the whites
of three eggs and as much double refined sugar as will sweeten it to
your tast[e]
stir these together but not to beat them so put it into the boyling
liquor   when you see it begin to boile againe scum it cleane
then take it off, run it againe through your jelly bagg into your
glasses
if you please you may putt some slices of leamon pill [peel] in to
the glasses
you must be sure to put the harts horne and water into somthing
that it may be close covered downe
if you make it for sick people you may putt a sprigg of
rosemary in and what spice you please

A cure for a Cathrick [cataract ?]
or skin growing over the eyes

Take pilgrime salve
dry it in a fine pan or upon a brick by the fire untill it be as hard
as a stone   then beat it into powder and searce it through a peice
of tiffiny or lawne
then put it into a quill and blow it into the eye for either man or
horse

A glister for a Fever

Take a pinte of possett ale and boile it in a handfull of violets
bruise a few Anniseeds to the quantity of halfe a spoonfull
then straine it and put in halfe a spoonfull [of] course sugar
if you have no violets put in two ounces of sirrup of violets when
you straine it   and give it blood warme at three or foure of the
clock in the afternoon   probatum

For a Canker in the nose

Take prepared tutia which is slaked in a mans childs urin
And Ceruse of each two drams and a halfe
five ounces of the juce of house leek
rub it in a lead morter three dayes three houres in a day
then put more juce and do as before foure or five times
Annoint the sore three or foure times a day

~~~~~~~~~~~~~~~~~~~~~~~~~

There is a plant called Hartshorn or Buckthorn *(Plantago Coronopus)* but this sounds
more like real deer's horn.   Pilgrim Salve is actually human excrement.
Sweet Violet *(Viola odorata)*.
Venetian Ceruse, also known as 'Spirits of Saturn', was a lead-based skin-whitening
cosmetic, not normally used in this fashion.   'Tutia' - see page 11.
Houseleek *(Sempervivum tectorum)* {pictured left} is probably what is being used here;
but what is commonly called Biting Stonecrop *(Sedum acre)* {pictured right} was once
known as the house-leek.

Banesters bag to purge Sharp ill humors

Take two Ounces of dry Egrymony Roots and leaves one ounce of
harts horne. two drams of Sasafruss.

An ounce and a halfe of Ligmen Sanctem.

halfe an ounce of Annyseed and Liquorish of each an ounce:

a handfull of Reasons of the sunn all these being sliced and put in
a bolter bag in a gallon and a halfe of ale and a stone putt into the
bagg to make it sink

begin to drink of it two days after it is tunned halfe a pinte in a
morning fasting and at two in the after noone

if the dayes be short drink that which should be in the afternoone
att ten before dinner

you need not keep in but drink it in all weather

Dr Woods rare Balsom for Coughs or colds or Consumptions or any Penumatick distemper

Take the best spirit of Sack that is possible to be had

And to every quart of spirit take eight ounces of Sarsaparilla being
cutt and quartered wiped and picked very cleane the quarters being
cut very short and free from any dross or foulness putting it into a
cleare but very dry infewsing glass

then power [pour] the quart of spirit of sack upon it covering it as
close as possible and so let it stand a month or more till you see it of
an excellent bright deep gold colour

then straine it out but first have redy pounded and sifted through a
very fine searce eight ounces of Gumguaicum which must be picked
from the least dross before pounded or sifted.

and then put it into a strong glass bottle that will hold three pintes

then pouer the spirit of sack aforesaid on it

And then cover it very close and set it in a warme place

stirring it twice or thrice a day till you see all the powder quite
dissolved in it which will be at least a moneth forgetting not in all

that time to shake it twice a day
then put to it full two ounces of the best indian or Peranian Balsome
shake it a fortnight longer but not set it to the fire but you may put it into the Sun is the best to set it in and when it is so don[e] stop it close in little bottles and keep it for your use
This is called the Rich Roman Ballsome
you may take thirty drops or more in conserve of roses or anything as you like going to bed but be sure you do not drink after it
you may mix it in the concerve by your taste for it must be very hot in the mouth for the stronger you take it the better

For the Convultion fitts in Children

Take a good handfull of wormwood and shred it small
And take as much Aquavitae as will moisten it
then boyle till the worme wood be soft
then lay it betwixt two cloths
so lay it from the top of the stomack to the navell of the belly
lay it unto warme

~~~~~~~~~~~~~~~~~

'Egrymony' = Agrimony (Agrimonia eupatoria).
'Harts horne' = Buckthorn - see page 43.
'Sasafruss' = Sassafras (Sassafras albidum).
'Ligmen Sanctem' is Lignum Sanctum, a form of Guaiacum (from South America).
The 'Penumatick distemper' seems to refer to blocked breathing.
'Sarsaparilla' = Sarsparilla (Smilax ornata)
The word 'searce' appears in several forms and seems to refer the use of a fine gauze cloth through which things are sieved (see page 42).
'Gumguaicum' is extracted from the heart-wood of the Guaiacum tree (Guaiacum officinale).
'Peranian Balsome' is Peruvian Balsam (Myroxylon Pereira).
Wormwood (Artemisia absinthium) - see pages 20, 33 & 38.
Aquavitae - see page 13

For any swelling and to dissolve and break and help a Brest

Take as much bees wax as an egg   twice as much fresh Butter
melt the wax and butter together then into it a spoonfull of pepper
grosely beaten and a nutmeg beaten a spoonfull of honey
threespoonfull of white wine vinigar
stir these together till it boyle a little
then take it off the fire and keep it perpetually stirring till it be cold
the[n] spred it on a peice of lokerum cutting a hole for the neple
[nipple]   dress it twice a day

For a Dropsy

Take every morning a toste of bred spred with sallet Oyle for nine
dayes   then take of clarret wine three pintes
of balme broome and bettony of each one handfull green
cut them small and put them into the wine and add unto it as
much sugar as will make it tastefull
one nutmeg and a few cloves beaten
stop it close and shake it often and after twenty foure hours drink
of it in the morning and at foure of the clock on the after noone a
good wine glass

A poset drink for the stone when you feele your selfe in paine

Take a spoonfull of English Liquorish   shred overthwart a handfull
of Althea roots   in like manner a spoonfull of Annyseeds bruised
one spoonfull of mellon or million seeds sliced
boile all these in a pottle of cleare posset ale untill the one halfe be
consumed and every night and morning that you are greived with
the stone take half a pinte thereof luke warme and put it into every
draught a spoonfull of the syrrop of Althea

To make the Lady Gaudys Eye water

Lapis Caliminaris a dram in a whole peice

lapis Tutij a dram

white sugar candy a dram

white copperis a dram Aloes a dram

these be the ingredients

the Lapis Caliminaris must be prepared thus

burne it five or six times in a chaffen dish of quick coales till red hott

then quench it every time in a fresh spoonfull of white rose water then when it is dry beat it and the rest of the things together to a powder and then put them into a glass that holds nigh a pinte of snow water and when they be putt into the glass you must shake them for five or six dayes five or six times every day and then it is fit for use

This cleareth the eyes stopeth rheum

it killeth a pin an web

it is good for any blow in the eye

when you go to bed drop in two or three drops in your eyes when you be layd.

~~~~~~~~~~~~~~~~~~~~~~~~~~~

'Lokerum' appears to refer to a soft but stiff cloth.

'A dropsy' was severe water-retention.

'Balme' = Lemom Balm - see page 35. 'Broome' = Broom *(Cytisus scoparius)*.

'Bettony' = Betony - see page 28.

Althea = Marshmallow - see pages 27 & 29.

'Million seeds' were the seeds of the 'English Melon' or Pumpkin *(Cucurbita pepo)*.

'Lapis Caliminaris' - see page 11.

'Lapis Tutij' - I take this to mean something similar to 'Tut[t]ia of Alexandria' - see page 11.   'Copperis' = Copperas - see page 17.

'Aloes' - *Aloe vera*.

A 'chaffen dish' was a heated dish with coals underneath it.

Snow water, I take to be, exactly what it says.

Webster's dictionary of 1913 describes 'Pin an[d] web' as two eye diseases, once believed to be one; Caligo & Pterygium.

The receipt to make Dʳ Buckworths Lozengers

Loafe sugar two pounds
powder of Anniseeds two ounces
powder of Elicampane halfe an ounce
one grayne of musk
of Amber a quarter of an ounce
of Angellico roots powdered
a quarter of an ounce,
powder of liquorish halfe an ounce,
powder of brimstone
halfe a quarter of an ounce,
powder of orris a quarter of an ounce
six pennyworth of safforn

Angelica

To make a very good Lozing for a tickling cough

Take of nutmeg one dram
mastick and gum Araback of each one dram and halfe
frankincence two drams   myrrh one scruple
conserve of red roses halfe an ounce with a sufficient quantaty of
white sugar dissolved in red rose water
make up these ingredients into Lozinges of which keep one in your
mouth when you go to rest

~~~~~~~~~~~~~~~~~~~~~~~~

Doctor Buckworth's lozenges are well documented - they were reputed to cure all
manner of complaints in the seventeenth century, including the plague.
'Elicampane' - see page 12.   'Orris' = *Iris florentina* or *I. germanica*)
Musk may mean real musk from the musk deer. Alternatively, herbalists used Musk
Root *(Ferula sumbul)* and Musk Mallow (or Musk seed) *(Hibiscus abelmoschus)*.
I assume the amber he uses is grated from genuine fossil resin.
'Angellico' = Angelica *(angelica archangelica)*.
Frankincense *(Boswellia sacra)* is mentioned a number of times in this book and
shows how freely he used rare and exotic ingredients.
Saffron (see page 32) and myrrh (see page 30) appear several times.

A Plaster for paine of the Back

Take halfe an ounce of Diapalmer
half an ounce of penishences
a quarter of an ounce of oxycrocium
A quarter of an ounce of Diackcolum
put them all into a thing together and melt them and spread a
plaster as the place requiers

The Green Oyntment

Take veruaine mallows smallage Howsleek the inward bark of
elder a[n]d leaves and mary gold leaves
all shred small of each two handfulls
boile all these in two pound of porke suit with continuall
stiring hours
then put in halfe a pound of turpentine
when that is disolved straine out the herbes and reserve the
oyntment for your use

~~~~~~~~~~~~~~~~~~~~~~~~~~~

'Diapalmer' and 'penishences' remain something of a mystery.
'Oxycroceum' (see page 1) refers to a preparation of saffron (from *Crocus sativus*) in vinegar.
'Diackcolum' = Diachylon, which is boracic acid, lead stearate and starch.
'Veruaine' = Vervain *(Verbena officinalis)*.
'Mallows' refers to the Common Mallow *(Malva silvestris)*.
'Mary gold' would be the traditional Garden Marigold *(Calendula officinalis)*.

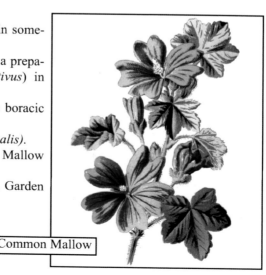

Common Mallow

49

To make the best Green Oyntment

Take green Sage and reue of each one pound
bay leaves and wormwood of each half a pound
of rosemary tops a great handfull;
of deere suett and sheeps suet newly taken out of the sheep three
pounds
the best oyle of olive three pintes;
chymicall oyle of spike one ounce,
the hearbs and suet must be shred together very small and then
beaten in a stone morter with great labour untill it be in one
substance as past[e]
then put it in a new earthen pot that is well glased and put in your
oyle olive,
then work it well with your hand
then binde it well over with double paper that no aier enter and let
it stand in a coole celler seven dayes.
then put it forth into a brasse pan and set it on a soft fire of coales.
and let it boile very soberly for two or three hours gently
stiring it untill the hearbs begin to parch and crisp
then take it from the fire and straine it through a strong new canvis
cloath.
then stir in your oyle of spicke and put your oyntment into well
glased gally pots and when it is cold bind them close over with a
bladder and leather

~ ~ ~ ~ ~ ~ ~ ~ ~

'Green Sage' probably means *Selvia officinalis*.
'Reue' = Rue (see page 9)
'Oyle of spike' (also 'spicke') is probably the essential oil distilled from the Spike Lavender plant (*Lavendula augustifolia {spica officinalis}*), pictured right.

50

For a convultion fitt

Take the roote of Centuary beaten to powder as much as will lay
upon a single twopence and give it to the party so payned in two
spoonfulls of faire water a little before the fitt cometh and so
continue it till the party be well.
And let the crowne of the head be rubbed with a lyttle oyle of
Amber and also the temples and take two pennyworth of Awseafetid
and hang it in a bagg at the stomacke
these you may have at the Apothecaryes shopp and by Gods help it
will cure the party so grieved.

A Receipt for the Rickets or the Riseing of the mother

Take a pound of may butter fresh out of the churne without
washing or salting   take a good handfull of cammomile
take bay leaves topps or leaves a good handfull
one handfull of red sage,   one handfull of featherfew
one handfull of green lavender   one handfull of rosemary topps
take all these after they be pickt   wipe them very cleane
chopp them small then beat them in a morter
then take a new pipkin   put in the butter and all these hearbes
set them on a soft fire
let them boile softly till they looke very green and the hearbs thick;
then take it of the fire and straine it as hard as you can into a pott
let the child be anointed every night by a good fire from neck to
foote and wipe your hands cleane in the cloth you lay it in and
shift it as seldome as you can

~~~~~~~~~~~~~~~~~~~~~~~~~~~

Oil of amber *(Oleum succini)* was a fine oil procured by the destructive distillation
from spirit of amber and was used as an antihysteric.
'Awseafetid' was Asafetida, also known as 'Food of the Gods' & 'Devil's Dung'.
It was a resin produced from the plant *Ferula foetida*.

To make vinigar

Take two pound of Allagant Raisons and put into a gallon of spring water and proportionable put it into a Vessell with iron hoops to keep it according as you have occation

An Excellent Receipt for a Rume in the Eyes

Take Adders tongue eyebright housleek and Agrimonie of each one handfull and a quarter   so much of Selendine
these herbes being cleaned and dry shop [chop] and stamp them and put them into one pound of May butter and halfe a pinte of the best sallet oyle and boile or stew them gently over a soft fier for the space of halfe an hour
And when it is coole enough straine out the liquor
then set it over the fire and let it simmer and scum it.
and night and morning put one drop into each eye
And if the eye lids be red swelled or painfull then anoint them a little therewith   probatum est [it is approved]

For a Glister

Posset Ale a quart
boile in it a handfull of mercury and mallowes and halfe a handfull of cammomile flowers and as much mugwort and a few Annyseedes and fennell seeds and two or three sticks of liquorish
and when they be boiled to the halfe straine the liquor out from the hearbs and take as much as is sufficient for a glister and mix with it three spoonfulls of course sugar and a peece of butter and apply it to morrow morning

~~~~~~~~~~~~~~~~~~~~~~~~~~~~

Adders tongue is a fern *(Ophioglossum vulgatum).* Eyebright (see page 19).
'Agrimonie' (Agrimony), 'Selendine' (Celandine), 'housleek' (House-Leek), 'Mercury', 'mallowes' (Mallows), cammomile (Chamomile), aniseed & fennel have been mentioned a number of times already. Mugwort is *Artemisia vulgaris.*

To dress a Dove House

Assafetida two ounces   a pound of coming seed
oyle of spike sixpenny worth
infuse the Assafetida three dayes in chamberlye
then boile it with the coming seed in three quarts of lye about a
quarter of an hour
then put in your oyle of spike and wash all the holes: being first
made clean

The dovecot at Felbrigg House, Norfolk

~~~~~~~~~~~~~~~~~~~~~~~~~~

Assafetida (see page 51).
'Coming seed' is Cumin seed (see page 37).
'Oyle of spike' (see page 50)
'Lye' was an old word for caustic soda.

For a Consumptive cough

Take four sheepes hearts splitt in quarters
wash cleane and dried in a lining cloth
put them in an earthen pott   And upon them one pinte of the best
red rose water and as much old mallago sack
four ounces of cap[e] dates, eight ounces of white sugar candy
powdered,   lye over the pott with a double browne paper and put
it into the oven with browne bread
when you take it out of the oven straine it out hard and let it stand
still untill it be cold
then take of the fatt putting to it eight ounces more of white sugar
candy powdered
then sett it over a gentle fire untill the sugar candy be dissolved
it will then become a sirrup of which take four spoonefulls every
morneing and night warmed and fast an hour after it in the
morneing

The Basilicon Emplaster which is good
for paine Straine old or new

Take yellow wax sliced thin black soft pitch black rosin grosly
poudered of each a pound
vennis or commen turpentine oyle of olive of each two ounces
melt all of them together with a gentle fire except the
turpentine
then take them away from the fire and presently add the
turpentine and mix all well together
then power it all into a paile of cleane water,
work it in the water and out of the water into roles for your use:

~~~~~~~~~~~~~~~~~~~~~~~~

'Mallago sack' means strong wine from the port of Malaga in Spain.
Pitch, wax, rosin and turpentine in various forms appear regularly throughout this book.

For a paine or a straine

Take brandy of the best and oyle of lillyes mixed together:
well bathed in will in a short time ease you of your paine

For a Cough

Take a quart of honey and heate it up untill the skim arise and
then take it of cleane
then put to it a quarter of a pinte of hysop water and skim it
againe and put to it one ounce of liquorish in powder   one ounce
of Annyseeds in powder   one ounce of carraway seeds in powder
halfe an ounce of elicampany in powder
and boile them together moderatly a quarter of an hour
and then put it into a pot and put to it two ounces of red ston
sugar canded beaten to powder
and stir them well together
and take so much as a wallnutt at a time
that is to say in the morning fasting and at bedtime

For a breast that is swelled and hard

Take soap and honey and a little urine and boile them together
anoint the breast.

To stop the bleeding of a cut

Take parsly and stamp it and lay some course sugar on
For a great pain take the gall of an ox and bath it

~~~~~~~~~~~~~~~~~~~~~~~~~~~~

'Oyle of lillyes' would have beeen produced from either the Madonna Lily *(Lilium candidum)* or the Water Lily *(Nymphaea alba).*
'Hysop water' (see page 15).   'Elicampany' = Elecampane (see page 12).
'Carraway' = Caraway *(Carum carvi).* Liquorice, used in this country since at least the thirteenth century was usually obtained fromthe root of *Glycyrrhiza glabra.* Medicinal use of aniseed, from the seeds of *Pimpinella anisum,* has a similarly long history.

To make Aquamirabilis

Takes Quibes Gallingall Cardimones Melliat Flowers Cloves
Mace Ginger Cinomon Nutmegs of each halfe an ounce a peice
bruise them then steep them twenty foure hours in one quart of the
juce of Sallandine And a gallon of the Spirits of Sack with two
handfull of spire mint and one handfull of Balme and one handfull
of Marygold Flowers
then still them with a good quick fire hiting [or 'luting'] your still
verry close with pasted papers and when you have drawn it all put
it all together and sweeten itt either with white Sugarcandy or
double refined sugar   which you please

~~~~~~~~~~~~~~~~~~~~~~~~~

This 'miracle water' is an unusual concoction. 'Quibes' remains something of a mystery, as does the purpose of the eventual distillation, though I assume it to be a form of tonic. 'Gallingall' = Galingale *(Cyperus longus)*, otherwise known as the Umbrella Plant. Culpeper uses both a larger and a smaller form to 'strengthen the stomach and the brain, take away windiness of the womb, relieve faint hearts and provoke amorous diseases.' 'Cardimones' = Cardamom (still one of the world's most expensive spices) 'Melliat flowers' = Melilot *(Melilotus officinalis)* - see page 20.

The spices used here are familiar enough, though at that time, cloves, mace, cinnamon and nutmeg would have been extremely expensive.
'Sallandine' = Celandine (see page 15)
'Spirits of sack' (see pages 30 & 54)
'Balme' = Lemon Balm (see page 35)
'Marygold flowers' = Garden Marigold *(Calendula officinalis* (see page 49)

The fireplace at Pakenham Watermill, Suffolk - complete with bread oven

bay falt beat together when it hath laine three
or four dayes rubb a little falt prewnello then
let it ly for a fortnight then boile it for your
ufe

To make collord Beif

Take a coft of beif bone it and lay it twenty
four hours in pump water fhifting it at leaft
foure or five times the laft time put no more
water then to cover the meat and add halfe
a pinte of Clarrett then let it run dry then

Wines, Preserves

and recipes

as you do Drawn

pott a good deale to bigg for the collor &
the fpice and wine that is left in the difh
with it and place it in a very hott oven. &
when it is drawn let it be almofte cold &
then take it out of the pot

To make Shromesbury cakes

Take two pound and a halfe of dryed
flower one pound and ahalfe of butter one

To make Cowslip Wine

Take five Gallons of water and to every Gallon put ten pounds of Sugar

before you set it on the fire you add whites of five egges and a half let it boile an hour continually scum being of it then take a peck and an half of pick'd Cowslips

bruise them in a stone morter a little then put these into a tub and pour the liquor hot on them

when it is blood warm spread some yeast upon a slice of white bread toasted and put in brew and let it stand twelve hours then take out the white bread

then put it into a vessell [with the] Cowslips and let stand three weeks then bottle it off

To make Ginger Wine

To six Gallons of Water put foure pounds of good Sugar
_____ [torn page] lett the Water boyle a quarter of an hour [before? (torn page)] you put in the Sugar and skim it well

then put in the Sugar and let it boile a quarter of an hour longer

then put in the Ginger and let it boyle a nother quarter

then slice in foure Leamons and put it into a tub to work

and when it has don[e] working put it into a vessell let it stand nine dayes   then bottle it up

To make Raison Wine

Take two pound of Raisons and a pound of Sugar
shred the Raisons and the juce of two Leamons pill [& peel?] putt
this into a earthen pott then take _____ [torn page] of water
let it lye half an hour _____ [torn page] fire and put it into
the _____ [torn page] or four days _____ [torn
page] bottle it up and _____ [torn page]

To make Elder Wine

Take of Elder Berryes what quantety you please and to them twice
as much water as berryes being first bruised
lett them infuse forty eight hours or sixty
then gently straine out the liquor   then boile it one houre
scim   after which add to every Gallon five pound of sugar att six
pence a pound & boyle it a nother hour and skim it as before
then take it of and coole it and work it up with ale ye[a]st as beer
or ale
tun it up into a vessell and let it
stand to the begining of Aprill
then bottle it up for Summer
drinking   a small wine may be
made by adding two pownd of
Sugar to a Gallon of liquor

To make Damison Wine

Take a vessell full of Damisons
[damsons]
then put in as much water as the Vessell will hould [hold] and stop
it close and let it stand so a fortnight
then draw it out and put in a pinte of white wine to a bottle of
liquor and put a quarter of a pound of loafe Sugar into every bottle
and bottle it up

To make Goosberry Wine

Take twenty five pound of Goosberries and stamp them very small
and put them close into a tub or pott and power over them six
pintes of boyleing water
cover them and lett them stand till the next day then straine them
into a tub or pott   then put eight pounds _____
[torn page] them when it is melted put it into a vessell
_____ [torn page] it is fine bottle it up
the sugar _____ [torn page] then eightpenny or
tenpenny _____ [torn page]

To make white Meade

Take twenty pintes of water and two pintes of honey
putt it into the water and boyle it all moste a third part in and
scime it cleane as it riseth
put in a sprig of rosemary
then take it of[f] the fire and coole it like wort and when it is cold
enough, worke it up like beer and when it have wrough[t] six hours
bottle it up

putt into every bottle a
peece of leamon pill
[lemon peel]
let the corkes be very
good and stop them
harde downe
you may drink it att a
week ould
it will keep three weaks
and if you will longer
alow more honey you
may keep them longer
and it will be stronger

To make oring [orange] Wine

Take six Gallons of spring water

put in twelve pound of the best pouder sugar and the white of an egg well beaten

put them to it to the water and suger cold

then boyle them together threequarters of an hour skiminge it as the skim rise

then take it of the fire & put it in the juce of fifty Scivill oringes [Seville Oranges] with the outward rine peared of clean

then let it stand till it be cold

then put to it six spoonfull of good ale yest and six ounces of sirrup of safforne [saffron] or Leamon being well beaten and mingled together

let it stand to work two days and nights and put in two quarts of Rennish wine [wine from the Rhine]

then put it into a vessell and stop it close and let it stand for a fortnight   then drow it into bottles and stop them close with new corkes   this will keep a yeare and you may drink it in two months

To make strong Mead

Boile your water an hour then let it stand all night to settle

then to every gallon of the water take three pound of fine honey mix them well toger [together] and hang it over the fire in a kettle and when it is pretty neare boiling put into the quantaty of ten gallons of water the whites and shells of twelve or eighteen eggs stir it together and when it boiles boyles scum it off and put in a little Rosemary and a pretty deale of Cinomon and let it boyle an hour and still scum it [as] the scum rises

then straine it through a cive [sieve] and it stand till it is quite cold then tun it into a vessell that it will stop it close and let it stand halfe a yeare before you bottle it and in a moneth or six weeks time you may begin to drink it

To make Metheglin [spiced mead]

Warme your water and disolve your honey in it
put so much in till it will beare an egg
then set it on the fire and boyle it allmoste an hour and scum it
very well
tye some cloves and mace and a little Ginger up in a cloth and
boyle in it with a good handfull of hopps and a pinte of Malt
then take it off the fire and straine
it let it stand till it is almost cold
then put in a pinte of good ale
barme and often beat it well in
let it stand to work twenty four
hours then tunn it up [in barrel
or cask] and let it stand a moneth
in the Vessell and then bottle it up

To make Cowslip wine

Take three gallons of water and put to it six pound of good sugar
boile it halfe an hour or longer and as the scum rises skim it off
then power it out and let it stand till almost cold
then take a little spoonfull of ye[a]st
beat it well withe the syrupp of the juce of Cittorns [some kind of
citrus fruit?] then brew it well together up and downe with a dish
in the liquor then take a peck and a halfe of clipped cowslips
put them into the liquor cover them up close and let them stand
to work two or three dayes
then straine it forth and put it into a Vessell and when it hath
don[e] working stopp it close and in three weeks or a moneth it will
be fitt to bottle
put a lump of loafe sugar into each bottle and corke it well and it
will keep a yeare

To make Elder wine

Take eighteene gallons of water and boile it till it comes to twelve
then put in twenty foure pound of sugar and the whites of six eggs
beat up to a froth
let these boyle together till it comes to nine gallons
then have ready in potts picked elderberries and lay them over with
paper and a saucer and put them into a great kettle and be sure
you keep them boiling And put to the neck of the neck of the pitcher
when they are enough take them out and poure the juce out cleane
from the berries but be sure do not crush and to every gallon of
your boiled water and sugar put in three pintes of the berries and
put it into a wooden Vessell
when you have mingled your water and juce together when it is
bloud warme spread soure brown to[a]sts well tosted of both sides
and spread well well with yeast and put them into your liquor and
cover it close with a cloth and when you think it is wrought enough
take out your tosts clean from your liquor and put it into a vessell
fit for it
And let it stand a night and a halfe a day open   then stop it up
with clay and if it has not don[e] working make a little hole with

Elder

a perser [piercer?] to
give vent for it to work
out   then stop it close
up and let it stand a
moneth before you
bottle it
you may doe [do or
'clo[s]e'] it with honey
if you please but it
must be pure Virgin
honey   a pound of
honey answers three
pound sugar

To make Mead

Take seaven gallons of water and put to it fourteen pound of honey an[d] two pound of white sugar   let it be boiled and scumed and then put in halfe an ounce of Cinoment and halfe an ounce of Ginger it must boile an hour
then put it into a tub to coole and when it is cold enough to work make foure or five white bread tosts and dip them in east [yeast?] and put them into it and let it stand twenty foure houers
then put it into the Vessell   And let it stand a week and bottle it

To make White Mead

Take eight gallons of Water and eight pound of the best honey two pound of the white sugar   putt them into a kettle and stir them together till they be dissolved with the whites of two eggs being verry well beaten and put into them: then boile it three quarters of an hour with continuall skimming of it;   then put it into an earthen pott with a tapp that hath eight leamons shred.   foure of them with the rines off and eight races of ginger shred and fourty Cloves   putt in your Meade as soone as you take it off of the fire. then let it stand till it be milk warme and put in six small whitebread tosts and kiver it downe verry close And in a week it will be fit for to bottle ꝸ in a nother week it will be fitt for to drink

How to pickle Cucombers

First wipe your cucombers with a wooling cloth
then b[u]y the best wine vinegar you can gett
then lay a layer of cucombers and a layer of dill and a little whole
pepper and a little salt and do so to way layer.
and let them stand eight or nine dayes.
then power them into a brass thing and boyle them halfe a quarter
of an hour then power them into the same pott againe and tye them
downe close
you must serve them thryce so. but the last two times you must
give them but a floo or two if they cambe you must heat the liquor

To pickle Spratts or Herrings

Take your spratts cleane washed and dryed in a cloath and cutt of
the heads and gip them haveing Allspice and pepper grossly beaten
mix them with some salt   then strow some in the bottom of the
pott. and lay a layer of sprats.   and strew some more spice
then lay another layer of spratts, and so do untill you have filled
your pott
then strow some more spice on the top and fill it up with
vinigar, and tye a double paper over them and put in a course
past[e] over that
this must be putt into the oven when you put in your fine bread

To make a Tansey

Take a pinte and a halfe of creame
beat up thirty five eggs leave out fifteen whites
grate in halfe a pound of sugar roles
grate a nutmeg in   put in a glass of sack
mix them alltogether with the eggs and the juce of spiniage and
other hearbs then straine them   stifen it in the pan and turne it
into a plate   garnish it with leamon and oriniges

To force a Legg of Mutton or veale

Cutt your meat open on the wrong side and take the meat out and
beate it like a paste
then shred a quarter of a pound of beif suit and mix them together
season it with sweet hearbs and pepper and salt and nutmeg   And
with the yolkes of two eggs.
then put it in againe where it came out and sowe it up.
then make sauce for it with white wine and gravie and Anchovis a
shallot sliced leamon and onion pricked with cloves put in a blade
of mace and a little nutmeg: and salt   then sett it over the fire and
draw them up thick with butter and if the sauce be not thick
enough put in a yolke of one egg and then power it on the meat

To stew a Hare

Heat her well in her blood and
put her in a stew pan and a few
cloves and a pint of faire water
and two or three shellots [shallots]
let it stand till it be tender
then put in halfe a pound of fresh
butter two Anchovis
then dish it up

To pickle Harty Choakes

Lay your harty choakes [artichokes] in water two hours to take out
the bitterness of the outward leaves
then boyle them in water and salt and a little vinigar
boyle them till the leaves come off and they be tender
draine them from the water when they boile which must be in
vinigar while they look green
so keep them in a strong pott covered close

To make Sirrup of Cammomile

Take Cammomile or calomel and shred it fine
putt it into a wide mouth jugg
crowd it that it receve not too much water
then fill up the jugg with runing water and stop the mouth with
course paste setting it into the oven with household bred. let it
stand as long as the bred, then straine out the juce and boyle it up
with hard sugar
you need not boyle it to a sirrup unless you would have it keep all
the yeare
skim it very clean   this is to be taken in a mornings draught in Ale
beer or broth & so likewise in the after noon fasting an hour after
it useing moderate exercise
this is excellent to cleance the spleene which causeth
mallancholliness

To make Flomery

Take a pinte of the best Oatmeale and pick it and dry it very well
in the oven;   the next day after you have drawn your houshold
bred.   then beat it fine and put to it six pintes of spring water.
stir it together
the next day power out the cleare and put in the same quantity that
you powered off of fresh water and so do two or three dayes
then power of about halfe the quantity of the cleare water and
straine the other
it must be about the thickness of milk or creame
then boyle it keeping it continually stiring one way
when it is come from the skillett tis enough
then power it into coffie dishes or thin earthen dishes untill it be
cold and then it will be thick Gelly
you may turne it out with a knife
dish it and eat it in what liquor you please wine sider or beere

To preserve Goosberries

To eight ounces of goosberries put ten ounces of sugar and seaven spoonfulls of water
boyle them as fast as you can and when they look cleare they are enough.

To preserve Rasberries whole

Take a pound of the fa[i]rest Rasberries picked from their stalkes
take their weight in fine sugar beaten very small
to every pound of sugar take a quarter of a pinte of water
sett it on a quick fire and let it boile till the skim rise and skim it cleane
then put in the rasberries and let them boile as fast as you can
then shake them gently and sett them againe
so continue untill untill they look clear takeing off the skum as it rise

To make Dias Salony
otherwise called cleare cakes

Take Rasberries and put them in a stone jugg and putt them into a pott of boyleing water and ever as they do dissolve power out the liquor from them
take a pinte of that liquor and putt it into a posnett
then take a pound of sugar and put it in an other posnett with as much water as will melt it
then boile that to a candy height and boile the sirrup in another posnett
then put them hott together
then putt them into a glass plate made like marmolet boxed   then sett them in a warme oven or stove one week and turn dry and they will be a[s] cleare as christall candied without and moyst within

To preserve Apricocks

Take a pound of Refined Sugar and beat it very fine
take a pound of Apricocks when they are of a pale yellow ripeness;
pare them and stone them then strow some of your fine beaten
sugar over them, and when you have don them all strow on the rest
of your sugar. saveing one little handfull   then cover them and let
them stand three or foure hours;   when you finde pretty store of
sirrup amongst your Apricocks sett them over a reasonable fire and
turne them very gently continually till the sugar all be melted and
let them boyle a pretty while softly strowing some of the handfull of
the sugar you saved turning them continually
when you see they begin to look cleare and think they be halfe don
take them out and lay them one by one in a dish and still as you
put them in strow a little sugar upon them and when they are
taken out then power your warme surrop through a strainer
so let them stand till the next day then boyle them pretty soft upon
a quick fire
still turne them and take the skum of them as it rise and when they
look cleare take them up and lay them as whole as you can
then boile your sirrup halfe an hour very quick

then power it through
a strainer upon your
Aprecocks; and so let
them stand till the
next day
so put them in your
glass   power your
sirrup on them
you may put two or
three more Aprecocks if
you please

'Apricocks' growing at Felbrigg Hall

To make Quiddym of Rubies Couller and Amber Couller of pippins that you may make it all the yeare

Take pippens and pare them and quarter them and leave the coares
in them and putt them in a posnett with as much spring water as
will cover them and boile them very leasurely untill they be tender
and till they sink in the water
then straine them through a faire cloath
And take to every pinte of liquor halfe a pound of sugar and boile
it till it will stand upon the back of a spoon like quakeing jelly
then power it into your moulds your moulds being wett before
then loose it round about the brims and turne it of upon a wett
trencher and wet your box and slive that into your box
And that you will have red you must keep it close covered and boyle
it very leasurely till it be as red as clarrett wine in a spoone and
then boyle it up as fast as the other:

To make Rasberry cakes

Take as much sugar as
Rasberries and boile your sugar
verry thick but not to a candy
and boyle your Rasberries all the
time that your sugar is a boyleing.
then take your rasberries and
putt them to your sugar and stir
them verry well
then let them stand on a soft fire
a little
then put them into sawcers and
sett them in a stove

in the water, then straine them through a fair
cloath And take to every pinte of liquor
halfe a pound of sugar and boile it till it will
stand upon the back of a spoon like quakeing
jelly then power it into your moulds your
moulds being wett before then loose it round
about the brims and turne it upon a wett
trencher and wet your box and slive that
into your box And that you will have red you
must keep it close covered and boyle it very
leasurely till it be as red as clarrett wine
in a spoone and then boyle it up as fast as
the other:

To make Rasberry cakes

Take as much sugar as Rasberries and
boile your sugar verry thick but not to a candy
and boyle your Rasberries all the time that
your sugar is a boyleing then take your
rasberries and putt them to your sugar and
stir them verry well then let them stand on
a soft fire a little then put them into sawcer
and sett them in a stove

To Cleare Sider

Take a quart of white wine and foure ounce
of iseing glass take it to an Anvill or iron wedg
to beat it thin. And put it to the quart of wine
in a flagon close covered let it stand so twel
hours then set it over a soft fire whilest it

To Cleare Sider

Take a quart of white wine and foure ounces of iseing glass
take it to an Anvill or iron wedge to beat it thin
And put it to the quart of wine in a flagon close covered
let it stand so twelve hours   then set it over a soft fire whilest
it disolves   then straine it through a rag
then put these ingredients to two gallons of liquor and just boile it
then take it of and scalding hott
put it into your fatt and stirr it
together and let it stand twelve
houers   then draw it out and
put it into your vessell
let it stand as long as you
please.
in twelve hours it will be cleare
in ten dayes you may bottle it
or longer if you please

To preserve Damasins

Take your Damasins when they are full ripe
slit them in the crest and to every pound of Damasins take a pound
of sugar and a little better [butter?]
then halfe a pinte of water and set it on the fire and let it just boile
And when you have skimed it cleane take it of the fire and put your
Damasins in with the slit downwards
so cover them and let them stand till they be almoste cold
then set them on the fire and boile them a little jently
then take them of and kiver [cover?] them and set them
by the next day you may boile them till you see the
sirrup be pretty thick and the plumbs looke pretty cleare
if you think the [this?] be not enough you may boyle them a
little more the next day.

To make white Liver puddings

Take three penny white loaves and grate them
then grate halfe as much hoggs liver
beat the yolkes of six eggs and three whites with rose water and
sugar
mingle all these together and season them with salt nutmeggs
Cinnoman cloves and mace
putt thereto a good quantity of suett shred small And a
proportion of currance
wet them with creame:

To Boile Samphire right

Take a peck of Samphire the fullest and greatest you can get
pick of[f] the stalks
then take a pottle of white wine and a pottle of water and some salt
put these to it and let it simmer very softly being close covered
then put it into an other pot with the same liquor
keep it close covered
it will take all moste a day in boyling being don softly

Samphire country -
Morston Quay, Norfolk

To make bred puddings

Take a quart of creame and boile it
then slice two or three Manshits [?] with the crusts cut off and
power [pour] the creame scalding hot upon it
so let it stand till it be cold then beat six eggs very well together
take good store of best suitt shred and some foure ounces of marrow
three or foure dates shred small

season it with nutmeg Cinnomon
and sugar and strowe good store
of curran[t]s upon it
mingle them alltogether and putt
it into the skins
if you please put two or three
spoonfull of Sack or rose water
into it
you must put your skins into
warme water to keep them from
breakeing

To make an Orange pudding

Take two oranges and paire [pare] them and boile them in three or
foure severall waters letting the water boile before you put them in
and when they are boiled tender and the bitterness out take them
and pick out the kernalls and take halfe a pound of fine Sugar and
beat with the Orenges till it is a perfect past[e]
And take six spoonfulls of creame the yolks of six eggs and halfe a
pound of pure fresh butter
mingle it all together in an Alabaster morter and then put it into
good puff paste and be sure the oven be nott too hott
halfe an houre will bake it:

To make little plum cakes

Take a pound of fine flower dried in an oven   a pound of fine lofe
Sugar beaten and cerced   a pound of currants   six eggs but three
of the whites   three spoonfull of creame   six spoonfull of rose water
A little beaten mace
beat your creame eggs and rose water together
then melt a pound of butter and put to them
then put in your sugar and flower and stir them well together and
put in your Currants

To make little seed cakes

Take a pound and a quarter of flower and a pound of double
refined sugar eight eggs takeing out two of the whites and foure
spoonfull of Rose water
then beat the sugar and eggs together an houre and a halfe
then stir in the flower by degrees
so put them into an oven nott too hott
remember to putt into your cakes some coriander or carraway seeds

To make a Carraway cake my
Lady Huchisons way

Take foure pintes of fine flower put in six spoonfulls of Ale barme
wet with milk but very stiff
then lay it to rise halfe an hour before the fire and after that it is
risen work into the paste three quarters of a pound of butter and
foure eggs takeing out two of the whites well beaten with three or
foure spoonfull of thick creame.
And a little Ambergreece and musk if you please disolved in it
when all these are very well mixed strow in a pound of carroway
comfits
bake it in a tin hoop in a pretty quick oven

To make puf paste for a pasty

Take three quarters of a peck of flower four pound of butter and five
eggs   breake the butter in small peices   mingle it with the flower
in cold water pretty stiff   putt in the eggs with it
work it all together And make it up quick
lay about two pound of suit finely minced at the bottome of the
pasty and so season it with pepper and salt to your likeing

To make French Bread

Take faire water and good Ale ye[a]st and wheat meale
make a spunge of it
let it worke to the height till it be ready to break
then take new milk and some more good yest and worke it into an
easy soft past or dough
then put it into a fine cotten or wollen cloath
let it ly till it is ready to break
then take it out and put it into dishes which must be warmed in the
winter and covered
when it is just ready to break in the dishes take it out and put it
into a very hot oven which must not be stopped but watched continually for a quarter of an houre or less will bake a penny lofe
A quart of milk will make one dosen and a half of bread or more
if you make your spung with [milk?] and no water it will be much
the better

To Pickle Turky

Take a Turkey and bone it whole and lard the inside of it
season it with cloves mace pepper salt
And bake it in a quart of white wine and a quart of aligar a little
whole pepper mace and two or three bay leaves and a peice of butter
keep it in this pickle till you eat it
three quarters of an hour is enough for the bakeing:

The best may [way?] to dress carps

Take your carps when they are alive and seale them and so thro[w]
them into water and mingle a little salt in a little white wine
vinigar and cut of the heads of the carps in the middle againe and
so let them bleed into the vinigar and salt what they will
have a care you cutt them close to the head for feare of the galls
them gipp them and put them all into a pan not to[o] big
lay the heads with the noses upwards
And then cover them with clarret wine
And what vinigar and blood there is have a care you make it not
to[o] sharp & to them put a handfull of time [thyme] and
peneriall most[ly] time   And two or three rases of Ginger out [cut?]
in peices and an onion or two cut in quarters

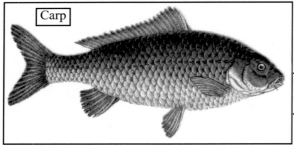

Carp

two or three Anchoves
and cover the pan close
and set them on a quick
fire
And let them boile very
fast not stirring of them
but have a care they do
not burn

when you finde they are
enoug[h] and your liquor about
halfe wasted putt in a good
quantity of thick beaten butter
[take it] of[f] [the] fire
and so lay your fish on the dish
with sopps of bread and power
the sauce on them
keep the other things back and
so serve them

be sure the liquor boile so much away that the sauce may be thick

To pickle Pigeons

Take the largest young Pigeons you can get and bone them whole
and lard them on the inside.
then turn them put them into boiling water to plump:
then take them out and make the stuffing of time
sweet marjoram savory parsley Anchovice onion
shred these very small together   then take mace nutmegs cloves
pepper and beat them very small and put salt to then [them?]
then mix your spice and herbs together
then stuff you[r] pigeons with it very full
And put to them a pickle of halfe white wine and halfe vinigar and
boile them in it halfe an hour
then take it of the fire and take your pigeons out and when they are
both cold put them in a pott to keep

To stew a Rump of Beif

Take a Rump of Beif and draw it over the top with leamon pill
[peel]   stuff the leane of it as full as you can of Oysters
then put it into a pot and just cover it with water
then set it over the fire to stew.
as the skum rises take it off
then put in a little salt and [w]hole pepper   a blade of mace
an Onion   a bundell of sweet hearbs
let it stew till it be very tender
then take it up and cover it close to keep hott
let the broth stew away till there be not above a quarter
take the fat clean of a quart of Oysters redy stewed to put it in the
sawce and two or three ounces of Butter
set over the fire to browne   shake the dredgin into it
keep it stirring with the back of a ladell
when it is browne enough put in a pinte of the broth
then put in your Oysters with two or three bitts of Anchovis
& stew them together and serve them up

A very good cold dish

Take a leg of veale powdred two or three dayes
parboile it a little and force it th[o]roughly with parsly and a little
time and leamond rindes minced very small in it and save it to eat
cold sliced   searve it up with oyle & vinigar

For Dutch Beif

Take a peice of Buttock Beif and lay it in hard water for a day and
a night shifting the water two or three times
then take it up in a tray and Rub it over with browne sugar
so let it lye all day
then at night wash the sugar of and salt it with salt peeter and bay
salt beat together
when it hath lane three or four dayes rubb a little salt prewnello
then let it ly for a fortnight   then boile it for your use

To make collord Beif [collared beef]

Take a cost of beif   bone it and lay it twenty four hours in pump
water shifting it at least foure or five times
the last time put no more water then to cover the meat and add
halfe a pinte of Clarrett   then let it run dry
then season it with cloves mace pepper & salt with a handfull of
time and sweet Marjerom
shred and bruise a graine or two of cutchineale and putt it in a
pinte of clarrett
after you have stirred it well together power it on the meat as it lies
abroad in some very large dish
then role it and binde it hard as you do Brawn and sett it in an
earthen pott a good deale to[o] bigg for the collor & the spice and
wine that is left in the dish with it and place it in a very hott oven
& when it is drawn let it be almoste cold & then take it out of the
pot

To make Shromesbury cakes

Take two pound and a halfe of dryed flower
one pound and a halfe of butter
one pound of loaf sugar
of nutmegs Sinomon cloves or mace as much as you please finely
powdered
the yolkes of five eggs with halfe their whites.
then lay the flower on a board and make a hole in the middle of it
And put your sugar and spices together and mingle them well
together and beat your water out of the butter and role it in lon[g]
roles and lay it round about the flower.
mould all these well together then weigh for every cake foure ounces
drive them broad and thin and prik them with a great pin. they
must be pricked with a comb all in rowes
after they are pricked with a pin between each rowe and so cross all
over againe
lay them on papers dried and flowred and baked in a
temperate oven

A Receipt to make little cakes

Take three pound of fine wheat flower
one pound and a halfe of butter
two spoonfull of rose water
three spoonfull of barm [balm]
a spoonfull of carraway seeds
a quarter of a pound of loaf sugar beaten
to powder
bake them after you have drawn small
stuff

Sweet Briar *(Rosa rubiginosa)*
from which rose-water was
traditionally made

To make pease soop

Take a Leg of beif and boyle it five hours with three gallons of
water and three quarts of pease
then take the pott of and straine your pease through a
cullander with the broth.
and when you have strained your pease set them over a brisk fire in
a clean stew pan
then put in a little handfull of spire mint a quarter of a pound of
butter a little salt halfe a pound of midling Bacon
one handfull of spinige halfe a handfull of Sorrill
put in unshred
let them boyle brisk for one hour putting in small bales of force
meat   make your force meat of veale and beif suit [beef suet]
mince it small putting in some time and Parsley minced very small
with a bit of onion
then for the seasoning of it take nutmeg Pepper and salt
work the forst meat together very well
then put in a french role a quarter of an hour before you take the
pott of
then take them off and dish it up putting in some fried bread in
little square peices with the french role in the middle of it and slices
of bacon round the dish

To Pickle Mushroums

Take a peice of wett white Flannell
rub the mushroums with it cleare and throw them into water that is
cleare and after some time shift them into another water
then take them out and put them into a stew pan with some water
and salt and set them upon a gentell [fire] close stopped and let
them boyle gently and putt them into a strong pickell with spices
shifting the pickell if it spots
yo[u] must not boyle your pickell

Bibliography

Whilst reference has been made to any number of people, books and web-sites, this is a short list of the books I have found the most useful.

Brown D.	*R.H.S. Encyclopaedia of Herbs*	first published 1995
Brown D.	*Herbal*	first published 2001
Bruton-Seal J. & M.	*Hedgerow Medicine*	first published 2008
Culpeper N.	*Complete Herbal*	first published 1653
Culpeper N.	*English Physician*	1826 Edition
Grieve M.	*A Modern Herbal*	first published 1931
Hulme F. E.	*Familiar Wild Flowers*	first published 1887
Johns Rev. C.A.	*Flowers of the Field*	first published 1907
McVicar J.	*Jekka's Complete Herb Book*	2006 Edition
Sambrook P & Brears P.	*The Country House Kitchen*	first published 1997
The Chemist & Druggist	*Pharmaceutical Formulas Vol II*	1946 Edition
Ward H.	*Herbal Manual*	first published 1936
(of Westleton, Suffolk)		

The Cloister Herb Garden at Laycock Abbey

The Fireplace at Kentwell Hall, Long Melford, Suffolk

Apothecaries' measures
1 grain = 0.0648 gramme
20 grains = 1 scruple
3 scruples = 1 drachm
8 drachms = 1 ounce

To help those suffering from the pestilence - By Sweat

Take Endive water a quart, Century water a pint, Ivie berries halfe an handfull bruised. Boile these together gently a quarter of an houre, and when you take it from the fire, dissolve therein as much Treacle as a Nut, and a little Sugar, also put thereunto three spoon-fulls of Vinegar. As soone as the Patient doth complaine and Nature being yet strong, give him fasting one good draught thereof warme, and let him keep his bed, and sweat ten houres, or lesse, as the strength of the Patient will beare. [A plague remedy from 1636]

Appendix

By way of contrast and comparison, I am including some of the pages of a notebook, once belonging to Dick Sargeant of Boxford. Probably written in the first half of the twentieth century, it includes herbal and other country remedies for horse complaints and mangement. Once again, we are insistent that no-one should attempt to administer any of these debatable remedies to any animal.

The writing is not that of Dick Sargeant, but as a wheelwright for a number of years, he would have known a number of people who worked with horses. The author was probably one of these people. What becomes clear in reading these few pages, is how little had changed in East Anglia over a period of two hundred years.

Mixture of oils for bruises or green wounds

Take tincture of myrrh oil of turpentine, oil of swallows and oil of pike and equal quantity of each shake them together in a bottle dress the wound twice a day

For a sprain in the footlock of a horse

Take the whites of three eggs
beat them well up
put them in a pint bottle
then add a table spoon-ful of sweet oil
shake them well up and dress the wound twice a day bandage it up with a flannel bandage give him gently exercise till he gets better

To make balls for the grease

Take rosin salpetre castile soap; soft soap; venice turpentine honey
aniseed powdered of each one pound 6 ounces oil of Juniper make
it into balls give each horse one every morning fasting and if bad
two one hour after half a pint of cold water one hour after
let him drink all he like and if his heels are very bad to make a
poultice with a half peck of bran half a pint of linseed boiled well in
two pints of water then mix it with the bran and hogs lard
put them on as hot as you can make them over night
take it off in the morning and wash the heel with soft soap and warm
water. Then wash it with the wash that now say one half-penny
worth of alum one half penny-worth of blue vitriol powder
put in a bottle that holds a pint and a half.
fill it with warm water after you have used that wash if there be
any bad cracks in the heel use a white lead ointment and buskin him
up. give him exercise. Repeat that till he is cured repeat the balls
every day till his better and 3 times a week till he is cured

For to cure a horse of a bad cold

take 2 eggs put in half a pint of vinegar blind them down from the
air 48 hours take and beat them well with the same vinegar with
2 table spoonfuls of honey and mix them together give that to the
horse each morning fasting an hour after give him a bran mash
and a half pint of linseed boil them in t[w]o pints of water
mix them well together put in the manger boiling hot
After this mixture take a handfull of hore hound ditto rue
ditto featherfew ditto mulle[i]n leaf ditto marsh mallows
ditto elder leaves ditto sullentine ditto agrimony ditto balm
then boil them in a gallon of water till it is wasted into three pints
in this 2 eggs to a pint and a half 2 table spoonful of honey
give him a pint and a half an hour after

For a horse that is feeble in stomach

Give him a quarter of an ounce of gentain [gentian] powder in a bran mash three times a week at night after water.
To clean a horses coat   one pound liver of antimony and steel of antimony   ditto sulphur   ¼ pound of nitre   ¼ pound of cream tartar   mix them together   give each horse one ounce three times a week at night after water   his diet the same as usual

For to mouth a horse

Take the liquid of spanish flies and touch the inside of his mouth with 3 or 4 drops,   let him go till his mouth be tender   then wash his mouth with cold water and give him a feed of corn.

For the cholic

Take juice of cinnamon   onions   dipent one ounce
long peper 2 ounces   ginger 2 ounces in three gills of warm ale

To make a horse lay down

Get some grey toads and hang them upon a white thorn bush till they are dead   then lay them into a ant hill then take them out and put them into a small stream   take that which separates from the others
dry them and beat them into powder: touch a horse on the pit of the shoulder to jade him and on the rump to draw him

To manage restive horse or wild colt

To make them stand still to be shod or prepare them to be sold at a fare you may numb them or stupify them; or sleep them
give him the tincture of opium, or laudanum the quantity according to the strength of the horse also ¾ ounce digitails or ¼ ounce henbane or black drops, from 25 to 40.

To make a horse follow

Take 10 drops tincture opium 15 drops oil aniseed 10 drops oil thyme Cinnamon rosemary and nutmegs mix them well together with 2 drams lunas or orris powder and apply it to the nose of the horse and you may do any thing with him

To make a horse cover when he is unwilling

First give him half a pint of west india castor oil to keep his bowels clean and open, a few days before you want him to cover
then a few hours before going to cover give him as follows
Two table spoonfuls of tincture cantharides
or two spoonfuls tincture lyttee
or oil of rape or oil terebinth
or ¼ ounce spirits nitre or ¼ ounce Juniper
if these should fail you may give him one table spoonful tincture Euphorbium
but this requires great care